HANDBOOK ON THE ART OF WASHI

HANDBOOK ON THE ART OF
WASHI

First Printing   1991

© Copyright 1991 by All Japan Handmade Washi Association.
All rights reserved.

Design : Yuji Kishikawa

Published by
  Wagami-do K.K.
  33-8 Hakusan 4-chome, Bunkyo-ku Tokyo 112

Printed in Japan

A Handbook on the Art of *Washi*
A Collection of Questions and Answers
Foreword
by Mr. Chosuke Taki
Chairman, All Japan Handmade Paper Association

Recently, visitors to *Washi* producing centers throughout Japan have increased. There are more individuals who wish to know more about *Washi*, those who desire to use more *Washi* and those who wish to make *Washi* by themselves. In order to meet this growing interest, the All Japan Handmade Paper Association decided to publish this "Handbook on the Art of *Washi*".

It is said that production and utilization of paper started in ancient China, spread through the Korean peninsula and was introduced to Japan. Due to the perservering efforts of our ancestors and after a long history, our present generation has inherited this paper from our forefathers and it has developed along with our progressive cultural life. Reviewing our environment, in the short history of western-style paper manufacturing, it can be said that the techniques have been applied more practically than have the techniques of handmade Washi.

However, in spite of the modernized present age, the unique *Washi* has, besides it's beauty and inherent strength, such qualities as warmth, softness, eloquence and attractiveness which are not commonly found in western-style papers and is one reason why it is making a strong comeback again.

Washi is born in clear mountain stream water found in many areas of Japan, utilizing strong fibers as *Kozo*, *Mitsumata*, *Gampi* (cf. Glossary) and *Asa* (hemp) and made with the hands of experienced craftsmen. Colored *Washi* put to diversified uses has highly increased popular interest.

With respect to this current trend, this book has been published to increase understanding and to gain more public support for popularization of *Washi*. The contents include general knowledge of *Washi*, method of production, history and usage described in simple language.

It is indeed my pleasure if the usage of *Washi* has helped in the areas of culture, hobbies and industrial arts.

In publishing this book, I must give my personal acknowledgement of thanks to those individuals concerned and those who have contributed valuable material and comments.

October, 1988

Chosuke Taki

CONTENTS

WASHI—THE SECRET OF IT'S BEAUTY

Question :

1. What is the difference between Washi and machine-made papers?   10
2. Why does Washi last longer than machine-made papers?   12
3. What is the secret of the strength of Washi?   14
4. What is the secret of the beauty of Washi?   16
5. Why is Washi more expensive than western-style papers?   18
6. What kind of raw materials are used for Washi?   20
7. How many days does it take to make Washi?   22
8. What is the yield of paper obtained from pulp wood?   24

WASHI—HANDMAKING IN PRACTICE, FORM AND COLOR

9. What is the reason for boiling the raw material pulpwood?   28
10. What kind of work is involved in speck removal?   30
11. What kind of methods are there to make the paper white?   32
12. What is the difference between "Nagashizuki" and "Tamezuki"?   34
13. Why is "Neri" required?   36
14. Why is paper made in cold winter weather better?   38
15. Why does paper peel off sheet by sheet from the "Shito"?   40
16. Why is there a difference in paper by drying on a wooden board and drying on a steel plate?   42
17. What shape and size of Washi can be made?   44
18. What kind of work is difficult and painstaking in making Washi?   46
19. Can anybody make paper?   48
20. What are the climate conditions necessary for papermaking?   50
21. How is the front surface and back surface of paper formed?   52
22. How is a watermark made?   54
23. What kind of material is used to impart color to Washi? The method?   56
24. Why are there blurring and non-blurring papers?   58
25. Why is Washi prone to be fluffy? What methods are there to prevent it?   60
26. How can bookworms or stains be prevented?   62
27. What kind of tools are used for Washi?   64
28. How many people are there currently who make equipment for Washi? How about their successors?   66

WASHI—ORIGIN AND PRESENT SITUATION

29. When and where was paper invented?   70
30. When was Washi originally made?   72
31. Tell us more about the history of Washi.   74

WASHI—IT'S VARIOUS USES

32. How has the use of Washi changed? 78
33. What kind of Washi is used for industrial arts? 80
34. How is Washi used in repair of cultural treasures? 82
35. What kind of Washi is used for calligraphy? 84
36. What kind of Washi is used for Japanese painting? 86
37. Tell us about Washi and printmaking. 88
38. What kind of arts and crafts of Washi are there?
    What sort of Washi is used? 92
39. Tell us about Origami (paper-folding). 94
40. Tell us about wrapping and Washi. 96
41. What kind of Washi is used in mounting? 99
42. How is Washi used in architecture such as in houses or
    buildings? 100
43. It is said printing on Washi is difficult. Why? 102

WASHI—PRODUCTION AREAS AND CHARACTERISTICS

Tohoku-Kanto Area 106
Chubu Area 108
Kinki Area 110
Chugoku Area 113
Shikoku Area 114
Kyushu Area 116

Glossary 118
List of Members of All Japan Handmade Papermakers' Association 124

WASHI THE SECRET OF IT'S BEAUTY

1. What is the difference between Washi and machine-made papers?
2. Why does Washi last longer than machine-made papers?
3. What is the secret of the strength of Washi?
4. What is the secret of the beauty of Washi?
5. Why is Washi more expensive than western-style papers?
6. What kind of raw materials are used for Washi?
7. How many days does it take to make Washi?
8. What is the yield of paper obtained from pulp wood?

Paper flower (mitsumata)

What is the difference between Washi and machine-made papers?

Today, most papers we see around us are all machine-made papers (for instance, papers used for newspapers, wrapping, books, notebooks, etc.).

Machine-made papers are mass produced continuously by giant paper-machines called Fourdriniers or Yankee paper-machines. Therefore, quality-wise, the papers are stable and highly qualified for mass use and consumption.

For instance, if the quality of printing paper called western-style paper here, is not stable, the printed matter shall not be uniform. In order to avoid this situation, machine-made papers are standardized paper made under specified conditions from the raw material stage. The paper is made continuously by machine so there is no room for the individuality of the papermaker to show itself. But reconsidering this matter, it may be said that such machine-made papers are not "enjoyable".

On the other hand, regarding *Washi*, the stages of papermaking are almost all carried out by hand. Only a certain amount of raw material is prepared and pulped at each individual papermaking plant. Therefore, although the same raw material, i. e. *Kozo* and *Mitsumata* is prepared, a small difference appears due to the individual or according to the place of growth. The papermaker uses this raw material and makes the sheets of paper one by one, so according to the papermaker, a difference shows up and this becomes apparent as the individual characteristic of that paper.

Of course, this does not mean that the quality of the paper may be uneven but the distinguishing characteristic is that the small difference highlights the individuality of the papermaker and makes the product more attractive and compared to mass produced paper, as each paper differs, it is completed as an "enjoyable" piece of paper.

Hitherto, it was said that the *Kozo* fiber could not be made into a sheet by machine, but that has become possible and a paper resembling *Washi* has been produced. From the consumer side, machine-made paper is adequate but once *Washi* is handled, the soft touch and subtle warmth which cannot be explained by words, can be felt. It is this feeling which will touch the heart of the person echoing the warm-heartedness of the papermaker who made the sheet of paper with devotion.

Answer : **Kou Hamada**

Why does Washi last longer than machine-made papers?

In a newspaper article dated February, 1979, it was reported that at the Congressional Library which has the largest collection of books in the U. S. , 1/3 of the 18 million collection i. e. 6 million books are so badly damaged that once they are loaned out, it will be impossible to repair them due to the advanced stage of deterioration of the paper used. It is said the same situation exists in libraries in France, England and other countries.

These books are publications printed from the middle of the 19th century onward using machine-made paper (western-style paper) utilizing wood pulp as raw material which happened to become popular at that time.

On the other hand, the oldest paper made in Japan is dated the 2nd year of *Taiho* (702) made in the areas of Mino (Gifu), Chikuzen (Fukuoka) and Buzen (Fukuoka/Oita) and used for census registration. The paper is still conserved at the *Shoso-In* Imperial Treasure Storehouse (cf. Note 1) located in Nara. There are also examples of old documents in museums which are older than 1,000 years and it is amazing to see the excellent lasting property of *Washi*.

The main chemical composition of vegetable matter is cellulose, hemicellulose, lignin, etc. . When making pulp, the most harmful component is lignin. The hydrophilic quality of lignin is low and if it remains in the paper it will reduce paper strength. If it contacts light or oxygen, pigmentation takes place which is the origin of discoloration which reduces the quality of the paper. For those reasons, a paper free from lignin is appropriate for preservation.

Also, in paper fibers, it is said

Drying *Kozo* fibers in the sun

that the higher the degree of polymerization (molecule length) and degree of crystalization, the paper lasts longer.

Wood pulp born about the middle of the 19th century in the west, was pulverized groundwood pulp made by pressing wood against a revolving abrasive stone face so the entire lignin content remained in the paper and was the cause of deterioration. It is due to this reason that newspapers left alone turn yellowish. Later, chemical pulp production started to dissolve lignin chemically and carried out delignification treatment by bleaching.

Vegetable fibers have a quality of absorbing water easily so if words are written in ink or printed on the paper it will run. Therefore, sizing becomes necessary to prevent running of ink. So rosin is added to the paper stock and also aluminium sulfate to maintain the pH (cf. Note 2) of the stock from 4.5~5.5. These elements become fixed on the fibers so the finished paper shows a weak acid reaction. Ordinarily, paper moisture content is 6 to 8 % so aluminium sulfate would cause hydrolysis and deteriorate the paper in the order of hemicellulose and cellulose which makes the paper lose elasticity. The paper becomes brittle and just by folding the paper a little, the paper cracks.

The inner bark fiber of *Kozo* and *Mitsumata* originally has little lignin and to eliminate that small amount of lignin, vegetable ash or slaked lime is used and the stock treatment is carried out under moderate conditions so the fibers are not damaged and a high polymerized (strong fiber) paper is made.

The fiber of the inner bark is itself longer compared to wood fiber, so the cellulose molecule is also longer which resists acidity. Crystalization is also high and contains an adequate amount of hemicellulose which is advantageous to paper strength so in regard to preservation of paper, *Washi* ranks highly.

However, recently on the raw material side, foreign inner bark fiber pulp or strongly bleached *Kozo* pulp with chlorine odor has increased. Also increased mixture of wood pulp or using a large amount of chemicals during the steaming and softening stage or addition of sizing (rosin) has taken place so preservation, with the exception of *Washi* produced in the traditional method, cannot always be good.

Note 1.
Shoso-In
Erected around 752 as a storage building attached to Todaiji, the temple housing the largest bronze Buddha statue in Japan. An Azekura-style structure (wooden storage building utilizing the expansion and contraction of wood to control humidity) storing treasures of Emperor Shomu (724-749) to Emperor Saga (810-823). Located in Nara.

Note 2.
pH
Chemical notation of hydrogen ion consistancy. The pH of water at an atmospheric pressure count of 1 and Celcius count of 25 degrees is a pH count of 7. pH count above 7 is alkaline and under 7 is acid.

Answer : **Akinori Ohkawa**

What is the secret of the strength of Washi?

If chemical or artificial fibers such as rayon or nylon or animal hair are dispersed in water and scooped up in a screen and dried, they would break up into fragments and not form a sheet.

But if wood or vegetable fibers are scooped up in the same way and dried in the sun, a strong sheet is formed.
Why?

Vegetable fiber has a property of "self-adhesion" and the fibers adhere to each other at a contact point between fibers. This property was discovered accidently and became the cause of discovery and modification of paper in ancient China.

In order to understand this property of self-adhesion, it is necessary to know what fibers are.

Vegetable fiber (cellulose) is formed from glucose. The cellulose molecule is made up from much glucose which is connected lengthwise. This cellulose molecule does not dissolve in water but has a property to work well with water (hydrophilic) and the fiber is a large collection of cellulose molecules.

Hydrophilicness means that at some place in the cellulose molecule there are some parts which have the same type of molecule as the molecule of water and cohesion of that part and water is easily carried out. Therefore, vegetable fibers work well with water and when fibers are soaked in water, they absorb water easily and expand.

After allowing the fiber to absorb adequate water and making it into the form of a sheet and then drying it, the fibers which have cohesion with water and the part in contact with the fiber changes into cohesion between fibers and though each cohesion is weak, throughout the sheet, cohesion is carried out in so many places that it becomes a great strength and a strong sheet of paper is formed. This cohesion of fibers is called "hydrogenic cohesion".

Compared to western-style papers such as newspapers, the secret of the strength of *Washi* is also related to fiber length. The length of *Kozo* fibers used in *Washi* measure in average 7.3 mm, *Mitsumata* 3.2 mm and *Gampi* 5.0 mm. Compared to this, wood pulp fiber length used mainly in machine-made papers are 2.3 mm in case of softwoods such as pine and fir and 1.02 mm in case of hardwoods such as beech, oak and chinquapin.

Also, from a technical point of view, the ratio of length and width of fibers (area) may be compared. The ratio is *Kozo* 510, *Mitsumata* 420, *Gampi* 490. Compared to this, softwood pulp fibers are 86 and hardwood pulp 60. This indicates that *Washi* shows a greater numerical value.

From such comparison, it can be said that *Kozo*, *Mitsumata* and *Gampi* are long and slender fibers but especially if a fiber is long, one fiber has many cohesion parts so even in that area only, a strong sheet of paper is formed. However, any strong sheet of paper, once immersed in water, tears easily. The reason is that which was mentioned before, water molecules permeate the cohesive parts of cellulose which is hydrophilic and cohesion between fibers loosens.

Answer : **Kou Amada**

Cross section of western-style paper

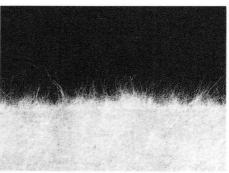

Cross section of *Washi* (*Kozo* paper)

What is the secret of the beauty of Washi?

Among papers throughout the world, *Washi* is unique, having both natural strength and beauty. The secret of this characteristic is that it is a manufacturing method that uses such raw materials as inner bark fibers of *Kozo* and *Gampi*, utilizes the medium of water and without any impurities forms a sheet of paper with only those fibers. This method is called *"Nagashizuki"* (Discharge papermaking, cf.Question #12 and Glossary).

Currently, handmade papermaking throughout the world is divided into *"Nagashizuki"* (Discharge papermaking) and *"Tamezuki"* (Accumulation papermaking, cf.Question #12 and Glossary). These are convenient technical terms used world-wide now but was originally Japanese craftsmen jargon which such experts as Dard Hunter (cf.Note) adopted.

During the final part of operation in handmaking of paper, ejecting water vigorously together with impurities is *"Nagashizuki"* and after disposing water, gently returning the remaining water backwards is called *"Tamezuki"* even today by local papermakers.

Operation of the latter method considers dressing up of the surface of the paper and the final manipulation is usually for makeup of the front surface of the sheet. (The screen surface forms the back of the sheet.)

The name of the two methods of papermaking which were only distinguished by a subtle difference of operation originally used the same mucilage and same water. But this has come to express a great contrast of methods by use of mucilage or not, difference of manipulation of water on the screen made of woven bamboo ribs or manipulation of the scooping up operation on wire mesh, etc..

So the *"Tamezuki"* method which was the method when papermaking was discovered in China was conveyed to the western world and if I said *"Nagashizuki"* was devised in Japan, it may give you the impression that the method of manufacture after entering into Japan was totally transformed. However, it should be said that it is a wonder that tools such as the flexible screen, etc. have retained their original form over these years. Improvement of tools and raw material has been carried out more in the west.

In the beginning, in China, long fibered flax (ramie fiber about 20 cm., hemp about 2 cm) was used as raw material so such processing as cutting or grinding in a stone mortar was necessary. When using rags, etc. different sorts of raw material were mixed up. In this way, processing of raw material and a tendency to mix different material was transmitted to the west.

In Japan, fiber length is about 1 cm. so intertwining of the fiber was easy and the most appropriate material for paper, *Kozo*, was growing everywhere naturally. Every year, first year branches were cut from the stump and work was carried out carefully to maintain fiber quality. In this way, papermaking developed, stressing fiber strength of *Kozo* and *Mitsumata* and material selection.

For instance, there was no effort to hide traces of the screen mesh and weaving thread but as grain in woodworking is appreciated, this became the point of appreciating paper and the technique for production of tools necessary for weaving of screens, etc. became more refined.

The technique of processing of patterns of flying clouds or water drops in the wet sheet was also developed. The difference of the front and back surface of paper is not only due to such ostensible reasons as contact with the drying board but is due to the composition of the layer of paper and of the tempo in forming paper. Not only luster, softness and physical strength such as folding strength but preservation endurance was also thus created. This method of papermaking was completed during the great cultural movement prior to the *Heian* period (794-1192) by development of national culture after assimilation of the Chinese Tang Dynasty (618-906) culture.

Note

Dard Hunter *(1883-1966) ; American expert on paper. Wrote many books on handmade papers, such as "Old Papermaking in China and Japan, and "Papermaking by hand in America". His books and collections are kept in the Dard Hunter Museum at the Institute of Paper Science and Technology. Atlanta, Georgia, U.S.A.*

Answer : **Shin Yagihashi**

Tosa Tengujo papermaking

Question 5.

Why is Washi more expensive than western-style papers?

How much do often used and easily purchased notebooks or letter paper found in stationary stores or supermarkets cost?

Compared to that, *Washi* cannot be found outside of specialty or folkcraft shops. Price is higher than western-style papers and it seems too dear to use. However, once the paper is taken in hand,

A *Washi* specialty store

Scraping off the outer bark

the weight of tradition and the warmth of the papermaker can be felt and when writing a letter neatly by brush on this paper, the feeling is that sincerity can be appreciated by the recipient.

The main raw materials of *Washi* are *Kozo*, *Mitsumata* and *Gampi* but let us compare the price of *Washi* made from the most popular *Kozo* and the price of western-style papers manufactured from wood pulp.

In order to make *Washi* by processing the black bark of *Kozo*, the yield would be 30%, but in order to make 1 kilogram of *Washi*, 3.3 kilograms of raw material is necessary. The cost of 1 kilogram of *Kozo* is approximately 550 yen so the cost of raw material only would amount to 1,815 yen. Besides that, the best white bark *Kozo* (yield from black bark is 47%) material made from refined and processed black bark *Kozo* is 50% yield for papermaking so the cost becomes very expensive, amounting to 2,700 yen per kilogram. To make 1 kilogram of *Washi* costs 2,700 yen plus 2 kilograms of raw material adds up to 5,400 yen. (costs as of August, 1989)

On the other hand, western-style paper is made by a continuous process from wood-chip-pulp-paper, so the cost calculation is difficult. However, supposing market pulp is 100 yen/kilogram, the yield for paper is 90% so the raw material cost to produce 1 kilogram of western-style paper is approximately 110 yen. You can see the difference by taking the raw material cost only.

Next, let us view this from a product efficiency standpoint. As *Washi* utilizes long fiber *Kozo* as the main raw material, it is difficult to make it into paper continuously by machine but is produced by hand one by one. Generally, a day's work (8 hrs) consists of only about 300 sheets. For instance, recalculated into the area of notebooks, it only amounts to 140 notebooks (30 page pad).

On the other hand, western-style paper is produced continuously by machine, so if a 3 meter width of paper is produced at a speed of 800 meters/min. and recalculated into an area of notebooks, it would amount to about 2.06 million notebooks per day (24 hrs.) which is equal to 18,000 times of *Washi* production.

Taking the raw material cost, productivity and the turnover of merchandise into consideration, the cost difference between western-style paper and *Washi* becomes extraordinary large.

Though *Washi* is expensive, it continues to keep up the Japanese tradition. Amid modern industry, *Washi* has been living continously and is close to everybody. Take a sheet of *Washi* in your hand at times, feel the imbedded warmth and use it preciously.

Answer : **Kenichi Miyazaki**

What kind of raw materials are used for Washi?

Many kinds of raw materials are used for *Washi* and in ancient times, *Asa* (hemp), *Kozo* and *Gampi* fibers were used. During the *Yedo* period (1603-1867) *Mitsumata* began to be used and at present, *Kozo*, *Mitsumata* and *Gampi* are the representative species.

Hemp is an annual growing shrub of the mulberry family and as it grew everywhere in the fields and hills, it could be collected easily so it was the main raw material for *Washi*. However, as preparation of the raw material required much labor, the amount used decreased gradually. At present, it is only used for a small portion of *Washi* such as for Japanese painting paper (cf. Question #36).

Kozo is a low growth decidious tree of the mulberry family and at full growth the branches reach over 3 meters. Easy to cultivate and an annual crop can be obtained. The fiber is thick, long and strong so it is used for such products as *Shojigami* (sliding door paper, cf. Glossary), *Hyoguyoshi* (mounting paper), art paper, *Hoshoshi* (thick calligraphy paper, cf. Glossary) etc.. As the end use is so very broad, *Kozo* is used most extensively as raw material. Total domestic production of *Kozo* was 419 tons (1980, black bark conversion) and more than half of that amount was *Tosa Kozo* produced in Kochi. Besides this, there are such *Kozo* varieties as *Nasu Kozo* (Tochigi), *Yame Kozo* (Fukuoka) and *Sekishu Kozo* (Shimane) which are cultivated in these various areas.

Mitsumata is a low growth decidious tree of the daphne family and the branches reach a height of over 2 meters and after planting, a crop can be obtained

Nasu Kozo

every 3 years. The fiber is soft, pliant, thin and lustrous and printability is excellent so it is delivered to the Printing Bureau, Ministry of Finance as material for Japan Bank banknotes which are known to be the finest quality banknotes in the world. Besides this, it is used for *Kinshi Ginshiyoshi* (gold and silver thread paper, cf. Glossary), *Hakuaishi* (gold leaf interleaf paper, cf. Glossary), Japanese phonetic character calligraphy paper (cf. Question #35), art and industrial art papers but the total amount used for *Washi* is very small. Annual total domestic production is about 366 tons (1980, white bark conversion) and the main producing prefectures are Okayama, Kochi, Tokushima, Shimane and Ehime.

Gampi is also a low growth decidious tree of the daphne family and branches of the grown tree grow a little over 2 meters. After planting, a crop can be obtained every 3 years. The fiber is excellent raw material, thin, short and lustrous but growth is slow and cultivation difficult so wild plants growing in barren, hilly land are mainly harvested. In the past, it was used in a great amount as raw material for base paper for mimeograph paper but recently, as copy machines have become popular, the amount used for such purposes have decreased suddenly. Currently, it is used for *Hakuuchishi* (paper for beating out gold and silver leaf, cf. Glossary) and *Maniaishi* (cf. Glossary) used for backing papers for sliding panels.

Beside these materials, according to the use of the paper, straw, mulberry, bamboo and wood pulp, etc. are used as raw materials for *Washi*. Also recently, such imported raw materials as Thailand *Kozo*, Phillipine *Gampi* and Manila hemp are increasing.

Note
Kami
means paper ; in a suffix form, the same character is read -gami or -shi.
Yoshi
means the designated use of paper, i.e. Hyoguyoshi would mean paper used for mounting.

Answer : **Junji Sawamura**

Kozo
(Black Bark)

Gampi

Mitsumata
(White Bark)

How many days does it take to make Washi?

Though used for the same object, the number of days it takes to make paper depends upon the condition of the raw material, equipment, method of raw material preparation and the number of employees.

Let us compare the number of days it takes for a person making *Seichoshi* (ledger book paper, cf. Glossary) by the traditional method using 37.5 kilograms of *Kozo* raw material and one making *Shojigami* (sliding door paper) by the present processing method.

Board drying in *Echizen* (Fukui)

The manufacturing process of *Seichoshi* (white bark) is as follows:

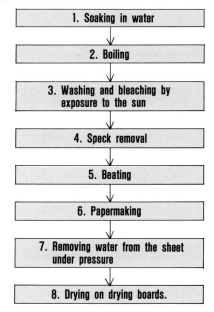

| 1. Soaking in water |
| 2. Boiling |
| 3. Washing and bleaching by exposure to the sun |
| 4. Speck removal |
| 5. Beating |
| 6. Papermaking |
| 7. Removing water from the sheet under pressure |
| 8. Drying on drying boards. |

1. *Kozo* (white bark) is soaked in water one night to make the bark soft.   1 day

2. Slaked lime solution is sprinkled on the *Kozo* material and then boiled. While boiling, the material is turned over and boiled for 3 hours. It is left in the cauldron until the next morning.
                                    1 day

3. On a fine day, the material is stirred in water to wash away the chemicals and bleached by exposure to the sun.   3 days

4. Each strand of fiber is picked up by hand and specks removed. At 3. 7 kilograms/day, it takes
                                    10 days.

5. 1 batch consisting of 2. 6 kilograms of material is beaten for 40 minutes and beaten again by hand for 30 minutes.   2 days

6. Making 300 18 gram sheets/

day will take 4 days. (setting the raw material to paper yield at 55%, 1,150 sheets can be made)
4 days.

7. The sheets made the day before are pressed while making paper so no days are counted.

8. If the sheets are all brushed onto 24 drying boards, 96 sheets can be dried at once. If the weather is good, they will dry in about 1 and 1/2 hour so 600 sheets can be dried daily.   2 days.

Sheet selecting, cutting and wrapping time remains but up to the drying stage, it will take 23 days provided everything is normal.

Process for making *Shojigami* is as follows (60% cleaning of the black bark)

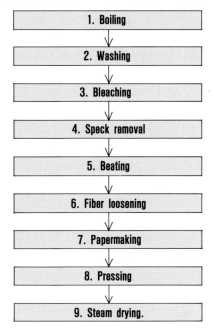

1. Boiling

2. Washing

3. Bleaching

4. Speck removal

5. Beating

6. Fiber loosening

7. Papermaking

8. Pressing

9. Steam drying.

1. and 2. The raw material is not soaked in water but after boiling in caustic soda for 2 hours, washing is carried out.   1 day

3. After washing, soaked in bleaching agent for 10-15 hours and washed again.   1 day

4., 5. and 6. As the raw material is bleached, speck removal is finished in a short time so these 3 stages can be done in a day. 1 day

7. 300 18 gram sheets can be made in a day so it takes 3 days. (yield 45%, 937 sheets made.)
3 days

8. and 9. Steam drying is carried out and 900 sheets/day can be dried. 1 day

Currently, *Shojigami* can be finished in 7 days.

For reference, reading the process stated in the *Engishiki* (927, cf. Note) of the Heian period (794-1192) to make paper from approximately 2 kilograms of raw material, it took 19 days for *Kozo* and 32 days for hemp to make paper so it can be said that *Washi* was a very valuable item.

Note
Engishiki
A collection of canons concerning court life, religious ceremonies, tax raising, etc. . Compilation started during the Engi era of Emperor Daigo(905), hence the name. Completed in 927. 50 volumes.

Answer : **Akinori Ohkawa**

What is the yield of paper obtained from pulp wood?

Kozo, *Mitsumata* and *Gampi* are the main raw materials for *Washi* and there is no great difference in the yield of paper obtained from each raw material so the example of making *Shojigami* from *Kozo* is most typical.

There are many stages of process in making paper from *Kozo* trees but at each stage those parts not necessary to make paper are not included.

The amount of *Shojigami* necessary to cover 4 sliding latticed doors is 220 grams. To make this amount 5500 grams of *Kozo* trees are necessary.

The stages of process are outlined below:

Kozo cut during winter (hibernating period of wood) is steamed in a wooden vessel (called *Koshiki*) with a diameter of 1.5 meters and 2 meters high. The bark is peeled off the steamed tree immediately and this dried bark is called the black bark (*Kurokawa*). In weight, this amounts to only 15% of the trees so the yield is poorest at this stage of preparation.

In the black bark state, much waste such as the outer bark, injured fibers, hibernation buds, etc. are included so it is soaked in water and softened and the waste scraped off neatly by knife and then dried. This is generally called "60% white bark"and becomes 9% of the trees. Next, the 60% white bark is boiled in an alkaline chemical and the unnecessary parts such as hemicellulose and pectin are dissolved so after boiling, it is thoroughly rinsed in water. Bleaching agent is added and rinsed again in water. This is the pulp stock and is 4.5% of the tree.

This is dispersed in water and scooped up and made into paper which in weight is 4.4% of the tree.

This paper cut into specified sizes becomes *Shojigami* product and is only 4% of the trees.

These are the general stages of process of making *Shojigami* from *Kozo* trees but besides this, due to the type or use of the paper, there are cases of making paper from black bark or by further processing over 60% white bark and using more high quality white bark.

However, in either case, the amount of paper from the *Kozo* trees is about the same and only a small percentage of the trees becomes paper.

Answer : **Junji Sawamura**

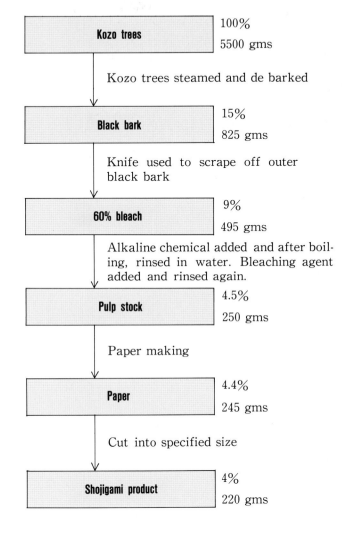

Kozo trees	100%
	5500 gms

Kozo trees steamed and de barked

Black bark	15%
	825 gms

Knife used to scrape off outer black bark

60% bleach	9%
	495 gms

Alkaline chemical added and after boiling, rinsed in water. Bleaching agent added and rinsed again.

Pulp stock	4.5%
	250 gms

Paper making

Paper	4.4%
	245 gms

Cut into specified size

Shojigami product	4%
	220 gms

Rinsing fibers in water

WASHI HANDMAKING IN PRACTICE, FORM AND COLOR

9. What is the reason for boiling the raw material pulpwood?
10. What kind of work is involved in speck removal?
11. What kind of methods are there to make the paper white?
12. What is the difference between "Nagashizuki" and "Tamezuki"?
13. Why is "Neri" required?
14. Why is paper made in cold winter weather better?
15. Why does paper peel off sheet by sheet from the "Shito"?
16. Why is there a difference in paper by drying on a wooden board and drying on a steel plate?
17. What shape and size of Washi can be made?
18. What kind of work is difficult and painstaking in making Washi?
19. Can anybody make paper?
20. What are the climate conditions necessary for papermaking?
21. How is the front surface and back surface of paper formed?
22. How is a watermark made?
23. What kind of material is used to impart color to Washi? The method?
24. Why are there blurring and non-blurring papers?
25. Why is Washi prone to be fluffy? What methods are there to prevent it?
26. How can bookworms or stains be prevented?
27. What kind of tools are used for Washi?
28. How many people are there currently who make equipment for Washi? How about their successors?

Paper maché masks

What is the reason for boiling the raw material pulpwood?

For raw material of paper, there is fiber taken from the inner bark of vegetation and fiber taken from wood. The inner bark part is in all vegetation and is located between the outer bark and wood core and its function is to deliver starch formed in the leaf to the parts below the leaf. However, according to the vegetation, there are some which have dense inner bark and long fibers and some which have not.

When making *Washi*, this inner bark fiber is mainly used and vegetation which has the most and longest fiber that can be easily extracted, is utilized. The vegetation which utilizes the inner bark fiber can be divided into 2 groups, i.e. from the wood family, *Kozo*, *Mitsumata* and *Gampi* and from the grass family, flax, ramie, hemp and Manila hemp. The inner bark of these materials are bound together by a substance called pectin.

Also, wood fibers of such vegetation as fir, larch, beech, mangrove, etc. are utilized and the fibers of these species are bound together by a substance called lignin.

These binding substances are removed and only the fibers are used for papermaking material. The method of removal is to add an alkaline chemical to the vegetable and boil it. Then both pectin and lignin are removed and the fibers become loose and separate individually. Here, we shall dwell upon the method of removing pectin from the inner bark of material used for *Washi*.

First, such chemicals as caustic

soda, sodium carbonate or slaked lime are added (in case of caustic soda or sodium carbonate about 20% in weight and in case of slaked lime, 40% in weight) to the raw materials such as *Kozo*, *Mitsumata* or *Gampi*, then boiled (the percentage of raw material to water is 1:20). This is called the boiling process. The chemical additive when boiling is generally caustic soda in case of black bark or 60% white bark and in case of 100% white bark, sodium carbonate or slaked lime is used. 2 hours boiling after reaching boiling point, pectin dissolves and becomes pectic acid which is soluble in water and the small amount of lignin content becomes alkali lignin which is also soluble in water.

The raw material after boiling is taken out of the cauldron and soaked in flowing water. After 24 hours of water rinsing, when the raw material is pulled apart by hand, there is no resistance and the fibers are easily parted because the substance which binds the fibers is practically all removed.

Answer : **Kou Hamada**

Boiling the raw material in a cauldron

What kind of work is involved in speck removal?

The labor for removal of bark and specks mixed in the boiled material is called "speck removal".

The pure white finished paper looks beautiful and gives a person a good feeling. However, if specks or dust are prominent here and there in the paper, the general impression is poor.

Speck removal

Papermakers try their best to make a beautiful sheet of paper free of specks. However, natural vegetation contains material, which should not remain in the paper. For instance, during the process of growth of vegetation, trees rub against each other and form disfigurements or when a creeping vine coils around a tree, that part remains as a bruise like a keloid burn. Papermakers call these parts "burns"and however much bleaching is carried out, it does not turn white and if paper is made with these parts left in it, it remains in the paper as unwanted specks.

Also, during the process of making the raw material by steaming the tree cut from the hills and debarking, the papermaker pays closest attention and endeavors to avoid any specks entering but as a large lot of material is handled at once, there are cases when specks and small particles of sand are mixed.

Then, during the stage of raw material preparation, it becomes necessary to remove these unwanted specks before beating. This work requires patience and perserverance as each speck is removed by hand.

There are 2 ways of removing specks. First, the raw material is placed in water and the specks are removed by spreading out the raw material little by little (water selection method) or squeezing as much water as possible from the raw material and spreading out the remaining wet stock over a board and remove the specks (dry selection method).

In either method, all the specks cannot be completely removed by one treatment and especially such specks small as needlepoints are likely to be overlooked. Therefore, speck removal is carried out on the same lot of material several times until only pure white fibers remain. There are cases when the "water selection"and "dry selection" methods are combined.

In the process of making paper, this work requires much patience and is most trying. One must sit all day facing the wet raw material and pick out specks as small as poppy-seeds. Especially in winter, it is so cold that one's fingers become numb but the papermaker continues his job by warming his hands in hot water.

Answer : **Kou Hamada**

What kind of methods are there to make the paper white?

A vegetable contains lignin and hemicellulose besides cellulose and these elements play the role of binding fibers together. Also, when utilizing the fiber, it is necessary to remove the non-cellulose part as mentioned before (cf. Question 9) when the raw material is boiled.

When the fiber contained in the vegetable is extracted, it has a white color. However, even though a strong alkali chemical such as caustic soda is mixed, heated and boiled, it is difficult to remove all of the non-cellulose material. If too much chemical is used, the fiber deteriorates before removal of the non-cellulose material and cannot be used. Therefore, an important condition in boiling the raw material is to remove the non-cellulose material as much as possible without damaging the fiber.

The fiber material which has been boiled and washed in water still contains non-cellulose material (poly-saccharide other than fiber, ash and resin). Therefore, the raw material remains brownish color and will not become white, beautiful paper. There is brownish colored *Washi* and there are uses for such paper but in order to make a white paper, it must be bleached further and made into more refined fibers. Bleaching methods are as follows :

Natural Bleaching

When using white bark raw material, after boiling and washing in water, the raw material is placed in a shallow water tank and spread out sparsely so it is well exposed to sun rays. This is

Paddy-field bleaching

Also, if washing in water is insufficient after bleaching and chlorine remains in the raw material, discoloration may occur which will also become the cause of deterioration.

Note 1.
Paddy-field bleaching
During the farmer's slack season, bamboo poles are placed side by side in the paddy-fields. Water is stored in the paddy-fields and the raw material is spread out on the bamboo poles and exposed to the sun.
Note 2.
River bleaching
The raw material is spread out in the running water of a shallow river and exposed to the sun.

Answer : **Kou Hamada**

the method to bleach by ultraviolet rays. Beside snow-bleaching common to cold areas, there are such methods as paddy-field bleaching (cf. Note 1) and river bleaching (cf. Note 2). By these methods, the paper does not become pure white but by pasting it on a *Shoji* (sliding latticed door) it will become white as the days go by.

Chlorine Bleaching

This is the bleaching method generally used presently. It is the method of bleaching by oxidization of chlorine which dissolves the pigment of the raw material and has the advantage of bleaching in a short time. However, the chlorine effect is very strong so while bleaching, it may also damage the fibers so it requires close attention.

What is the difference between "Nagashizuki" and "Tamezuki" ?

According to the *Engishiki* (cf. Question 7), there is an article on papermaking in a government established mill and papermaking during that time can be imagined.

In this article, the raw material, supplies provided per year and also the craftmans'work load is stipulated in detail. However, there is no mention of the currently used mucilage "*Tororo-aoi*" (cf. Glossary) and reading the process of raw material preparation, we can see that paper was made by the "*Tamezuki*" method.

Tamezuki method during the Heian period (794-1192)

For raw materials, hemp, *Kozo*, *Gampi*, *Kurara* (leguminous plant, cf. Glossary) and cloth (flax) are listed and the process of raw material preparation was to cut the raw material into small pieces, boil it in ash liquid, speck removal and beating it in a mortar. In this process, attention should be paid to the cutting and beating process. Especially, in the beating process, the amount of labor per day per workman was stipulated at about 500 grams for *Kozo* and 800 grams for hemp. Then, after beating the pulp stock, it is put into the papermaking vat and scooped up into a screen. After the wet sheet is formed, it is transfered onto a piece of cloth. To avoid adherence of the wet sheet, the wet sheet and cloth are placed upon each other alternately. This is called "*Tamezuki*".

The pulp stock used for *Tamezuki* is short fibered and when well beaten, dispersion in water is good. And when scooped onto the screen, the outflow of water is slow, so with one scoop, the texture of the wet sheet can be formed. In this case, a sheet of paper made from this well-beaten pulp stock shall adhere to the other sheet when piled on top of each other and will be difficult to separate so that is the reason a piece of cloth was placed between the wet sheets.

The main papermaking method of Washi is called "*Nagashizuki*".

Current Nagashizuki method

A mucilage called "*Neri*" (cf. Glossary and Question 13) taken from "*Tororo-aoi*" or "*Noriutsugi*" (cf. Glossary) is added to the *Kozo* or *Gampi* pulp stock and the pulp stock water is then scooped up several times onto the paper mold. After the wet sheet reaches the required thickness, the screen is released from the frame and the formed wet sheets are stacked upon each other.

In this method, cutting of fibers and laborious beating as in the past, is not necessarily required but by addition of *Neri*, the outflow of pulp stock becomes much slower than in *Tamezuki* so the pulp stock may be scooped up and several passes may be made on the screen so the base ply of paper can be formed without hurry.

Therefore, it can be said that the basic difference of the methods is that adjustment of the overflow of water is done by beating of pulp stock during preparation of the raw material in *Tamezuki* and by "*Neri*" in case of *Nagashizuki*.

At present, paper made by the *Tamezuki* method is used for woodblock printing paper or paper for graduation diplomas. However, the pulp stock used for these papers is the same pulp stock used for *Nagashizuki* which is not so well beaten. As outflow is fast, it is difficult to make a good texture paper so *Neri* is added. Therefore, these papers are not made from the orthodox *Tamezuki* method but it can be said to be a hybrid of both methods.

Answer : **Akira Ohkawa**

Tamezuki　　　　　　　*Nagashizuki*

Why is "Neri" required?

In order to make a beautiful sheet of paper, it is necessary to disperse all of the pulp evenly and uniformly in the water. For this reason, close attention must be paid to raw material preparation and it is important not to have fiber sheaves (fibers which do not dissolve but remain in bundles due to uneven boiling or insufficient defibrating)but however well the pulp stock is prepared, the fibers will not disperse evenly just by putting it into water and stirring it. Even short fiber pulp stock does not disperse evenly in water so it is more difficult to obtain an even dispersion of long fibered *Kozo*, *Mitsumata* and *Gampi*.

On top of that, the specific gravity of vegetable fiber is about 1.5 times of water so when immersed in water, it will sink immediately. It is at this point that *"Neri"*is utilized. It is usually called *Neri* or *Nori* (paste) so many people think that this used to bind the fibers when making paper. But this is wrong as the role of *Neri* is to help dispersion of fibers in water and does not have any adhesive strength.

Then, the reason why fibers disperse well when *Neri* is used, is that in the root of *"Tororo-aoi"* generally used as *Neri*, such polysaccharide as "Galacturon acid" which is easily soluble in water is contained in abundance. When the *Tororo-aoi* root is crushed and mixed with water, a great amount of viscous liquid can be extracted. This liquid is put into a bag and filtered to take the specks out, then put into the pulp vat and stirred together with the pulp stock. Then, as this *Neri* is a polysaccharide the same as cellulose, it is very intimate with the fibers. It wraps itself around each fiber slimily so the fibers do not entwine themselves around each other but are dispersed evenly in the water. On top of that, as the water itself has adequate viscosity, the fibers do not sink easily but will float in the water for a prolonged period.

However, viscosity of *Neri* does not last forever. Especially in summer, viscosity is apt to be lost so whenever pulp is replenished, *Neri* is also added.

The vegetation used for *Neri* is not only *Tororo-aoi* but the viscous liquid of the root of *Aogiri*(firmiana platanifolia), bark of *Noriutsugi*, root of *Ginbaiso* (blue bottle grass)are used and all these are of the same polysaccharide family.

Answer : **Kou Hamada**

Flower of *Tororo-aoi*

Root of *Tororo-aoi*

Why is paper made in cold winter weather better?

From olden times, it was said that "paper should be made in mid-winter". The origin of this saying is due to the fact that good quality paper is made in the coldest time of winter. When making *Washi*, a vegetable mucilage is used and this mucilage is a member of the polysaccharide family. The molecule form is long, like a chain (chain molecule). Therefore, when the thick liquid of *Neri* is picked up, it is stringy like a cow's drool. Technically, it is called "ropy". When this *Neri* is put into water and stirred together with pulp, long, thread-like *Neri* molecules spread out lengthwise and crosswise. Due to this action, the fibers are wrapped up by the *Neri* and disperse but when the temperature is high, the chain of *Neri* molecules break and becomes short. Then, viscosity gradually decreases and in the end, viscosity is lost and becomes the same as water.

When making paper in hot summer, the temperature of water in the pulp vat increases so viscosity of the *Neri* decreases rapidly and dispersion of fibers gradually becomes poor and *Neri* must be added and stirred from time to time.

Paper is handmade and the papermaker regulates the thickness of each sheet of paper by the feeling of his fingers and experience so it is better to work under uniform conditions as long as possible. During summer, it is necessary to add *Neri* from time to time and regulate conditions in the vat so efficiency is poor and besides, there is a tendency of the paper becoming uneven.

On the other hand, in winter, the temperature is low so even if water in the vat is left overnight, it still has viscosity the next morning and conditions for papermaking remain unchanged. Therefore, work conditions are uniform and efficiency is good, which is the reason why it is better to make paper during the cold period.

Another reason is the problem of decomposition. The papermaker makes about 300-500 sheets a day which are stacked upon each other on a board. This stack of wet sheets is usually called "*Shito*" and after a day's work is over, pressure is gradually added to press out the moisture in the *Shito*. This takes some time and approximately a day is required to squeeze out the moisture and according to the type of paper, there are times when the paper is left as the *Shito* for several days in a moisture extracted condition.

"Ropyness" of *Tororo-aoi* mucilage

As mentioned in the *Neri* section, when making paper, a mucilage of polysaccharide vegetation is used. Also, in the fiber itself, some polysaccharide remains. During the high temperature of summer, this becomes an excellent hot-bed for breeding of bacteria. When paper decomposes in the *Shito*, each sheet of paper cannot be peeled off when drying time arrives and even if it can be separated and dried, stains remain or outwardly the paper may seem to have no defects but when words are written on the paper, markings appear and many harmful after-effects show up later.

Answer : **Kou Hamada**

Why does paper peel off sheet by sheet from the Shito?

W hat amazes one watching *Washi*-making is the paper-maker's skill in finishing a uniformly thin sheet of paper. Also, what is strange is that when drying, though moisture has been extracted, the wet sheet can be peeled off one by one from the *Shito*. Why can it be peeled off and not adhere to the sheet underneath?

When making paper, I mentioned that *Neri* was used (cf, Question 13) and when peeling off the sheet from the *Shito*, this *Neri* plays an important role.

"Paper does not peel off if there is no Neri".

For instance, when fibers are dispersed in water without using *Neri*, the pulp cannot disperse evenly in the water and some fibers remain in sheaves and in some places, the fibers will not intertwine at all. If this pulp stock is scooped up and made into paper, thick and thin parts will appear and in total, uniform papers cannot be made.

If there is no *Neri*, water drips through the screen too fast so a uniform thickness of paper cannot be made as the fibers are not intertwined sufficiently and uniformly. If this kind of paper is placed on the *Shito* and pressed, then when it is to be peeled off to dry, the sheets will adhere to each other, the sheet beneath will also be peeled off together or a sheet too thin will tear.

This kind of phenomenon happens in reality at times even when paper made with *Neri*. The person drying the paper calls this happening "spoiling of the *Shito*".

"Paper with sufficiently effective Neri may be stacked one upon each other".

When making paper under such pulp conditions as the *Neri* being sufficiently effective and the fibers evenly dispersed in water, then the pulp water has viscousity so water does not drip out easily and pulp water scooped up into the screen can be shaken with ample time so the fibers intertwine well and an even paper thickness can be obtained.

Though a sheet of paper made this way is laid upon another on the *Shito*, the fibers of the upper and lower sheet do not intertwine so that is the reason a wet sheet may be peeled off one after the other. The sheet is peeled off the *Shito* in a wet condition so the chemical cohesion (hydrogen cohesion, cf. Question 3) which gives paper its intrinsic strength has not taken place. At this point, the wet sheet has only the strength of the intertwined fibers so it easily peels away from the sheets below with which it has no intertwining relation.

Answer: **Kou Hamada**

Peeling paper off the *"Shito"*

Question 16.

Why is there a difference in paper by drying on a wooden board and drying on a steel plate?

When you go to a papermaking village on a sunny day, you may be able to view the scenery of paper being brushed onto a large drying board and drying it in the sun. White paper contrasted with the surrounding greenery is a beautiful sight. However, behind this beautiful sight, heavy labor is taking place as the persons brushing the paper carry the large and heavy boards outside and then bring them back to the workshop, put new wet sheets on them and carry them outside again into the sun. Drying of paper cannot be carried out during bad weather causing inefficiency or during the rainy season, accidents such as the *Shito* itself becoming spoiled happens.

So the idea of the triangular dryer came about. This method is carried out by attaching steel plates in a triangular prism form and drying the paper by heating the steel plates with steam. Ordinary steel plates rusts easily and damages the paper so currently, stainless steel plates are used. (cf. Question 26)

By this method, drying is possible without consideration to weather, easily handled and saving space. Currently, drying of *Washi* is carried out by this triangular dryer.

"The subtle difference in quality in accordance with sun drying and the triangular dryer".

Is paper sun-dried on a board and paper dried on a triangular dryer exactly the same? The paper seems to have a subtle difference.

The difference is in the pliability of the paper. This is due to the difference in the drying temperature. Steam drying has a higher temperature so the moisture content remaining in the paper decreases and the paper becomes stiff. Therefore, regarding pliability, board drying is judged to be better. If left alone for an extended period, moisture content of both papers should become even but it is not so and it seems that this difference remains forever.

"Regarding paper strength, board dryed paper is judged to be stronger".

The next great difference is that board dryed paper is stronger than paper dryed by the triangular dryer. When cellulose is put in water, it expands by absorbing water. The rate of absorbency differs according to the type of pulp, pulp preparation, etc., but in any case, the paper made by those expanded fibers are dryed by brushing them on a board or steel plate. At the same time as drying,

the fibers start contracting but in case of board drying, the board and paper are both kinds of vegetation so the rate of contraction can be regarded as about the same. This means that when the paper dries, the board also dries and contraction takes place. Therefore, the most important point for paper strength, i.e. hydrogen cohesion (cf. Question 3) is carried out naturally and a strong paper is formed.

On the other hand, when drying by steel plate, the contraction rate between paper and steel differs and especially in case of the triangular dryer, as the temperature is standard, the steel plate does not contract but only the paper starts to contract.

For that reason, a part of the composition of the paper is destroyed and as ample hydrogen cohesion is not carried out, the paper becomes weak.

Answer : **Kou Hamada**

Drying by the triangular dryer

Sun drying by boards

Question 17.

What shape and size of Washi can be made?

I have often heard *Washi* called *Koban* (small-sized sheet) *Minoban* (cf. Glossary), *Hanshiban* (cf. Glossary), *Hanori* (cf. Glossary), *Zenshi* (full-sized sheet) and all of these names come from the size.

The size of *Washi* in the old times was 1 *shaku* 1 *sun* (33. 3 cm) × 8 *sun* (24.2 cm) and in Mino (Gifu) another old size made was 1 *shaku* 3 *sun* (39.4 cm) × 9 *sun* (27.3 cm). They were made one by one and the screen used at that time utilized miscanthus ribs and flaxen thread or horsehairs for the weaving thread which were not very good material.

Times changed and paper demand increased so Genta Yoshii of Ino-cho, Kochi endeavored to improve the papermaking mold and for ribs, he used bamboo and silk thread for weaving them. He also developed tools (1860) to make 6 or 8 sheets instead of the 1 sheet screen used hitherto. He also spread *Sha* (silk gauze) on the screen and invented the silk gauze papermaking method (1827) and was the forerunner of making such thin papers as *Tengujo*. (cf. Glossary)

This improved papermaking mold has been used for over a 100 years and even today it is used with no great improvement added.

The size of *Washi* generally made today are:

Shojigami	63.6 × 93.9	cm
Gasenshi	72.7 × 136.4	cm
Hoshoshi	39.4 × 53.0	cm
Udagami	31.8 × 45.5	cm

However, there are papermakers who produce small sized *Washi* using small sized screens

Making of the *Okadaishi* (lage size paper) in Fukui

making only one sheet at a time. These sheets are untrimmed on 4 sides and gives the impression of true handmade paper. According to the end use, there are cases when a cross piece may be inserted into a large sized frame and 3 or 4 sheets of untrimmed paper on 4 sides can be made at once.

Untrimmed *Washi* is also used for postcards, letter paper, envelopes, calling cards, etc. . In these cases, cross pieces are inserted into the frame and devised to make 24 postcards and 36 calling cards at one time.

On the other hand, there are large sizes of *Washi* used for painting and drawing paper and decoration paper. For the individual papermaker working alone, the largest size is the 3×6 *ban* (97.0×188 cm size) paper. For a special large size, in Fukui a 4 meter square *Washi* and recently in Kochi 2.1×6.2 meter ones have been made. In this way, large size and small size *Washi* can be made by adjusting the size of the paper-making mold but in either case, they are made one sheet at a time.

Away from the general common sense that paper is in sheet form, by using a formed and shaped wire net mold, a three dimensional art paper can be made. It is enjoyable to see *Washi* in various forms used in interior decoration. With the tide of times, the size and form of *Washi* will change according to the necessity.

Answer : **Kenichi Miyazaki**

What kind of work is difficult and painstaking in making Washi?

Today, in the *Washi* industry, shortage of successors is a major problem. I believe this tells what a hard job *Washi* making is.

Much water is used and heavy raw material is handled all day and it is not exaggerating to say that there is no easy work in any stage of processing. Here are 2 or 3 illustrations.

A white sheet of paper does not permit any impurities to be mixed in it. So speck removal work is carried out and the same pulp stock is examined at least twice (water selection and dry selection method, cf. Question 10). By sitting all day and examining small lots of fiber in water, damaged fiber and foreign matter are removed. Mostly, women are engaged in this job but as the job is difficult, most people give up immediately. At first sight, it seems easy as it does not take much energy but it takes much patience.

Also, the papermaker must stand on his feet all day and make paper by shaking the papermaking mold. The mold is suspended from overhead bamboo poles and about 10 liters of pulp is scooped up into the mold. Holding the frame evenly and making sheet by sheet while keeping balance requires much skill and at the same time is hard work which can be seen by the callouses formed all over the palms of the papermaker's hand.

The last stage of the process is drying of the wet sheets. When brushing the thin wet sheet onto a drying board or a triangular dryer, if the wind blows even a little, the wet sheet laps over onto itself and is the cause of wrinkles. Therefore, one must work all day in a windless condition inside, facing a steamed triangular dryer. Working while sweating heavily is really a hard job.

On the other hand, brushing the paper onto a one-piece board about 2 meters long is also hard labor. While being a repetition of simple labor, every stage of work requires long experience and much skill.

Handmade paper work requires hard physical strain while paying closest attention to details.

Washi is born from motion and stillness.

In a sheet of paper, the unmeasureable strength of a human being is concealed.

Answer : **Kou Hamada**

Scooping up the pulp stock

Can anybody make paper?

There are about 450 *Washi* makers throughout Japan. Among them, we seldom see young papermakers. At the "Young Mens National *Washi* Meeting" discussions on this situation, their exhibitions, and advertisement of *Washi* have been carried out and endeavors have been made to secure successors. However, not many persons desire to succeed to this work and there are production centers which are very inconveniencied by this situation. The Government promulgated a law in 1974 for promotion of traditional art and craft industries and introduced such measures as fostering of successors, developing of demand, etc. and is endeavoring to protect Japanese traditional industries.

With this tendency, recently, young people have a different image of papermaking. In other words, some can be seen as taking up *Washi* as an art and working with *Washi* as an artistic craftsman. Foreigners have taken a great interest in *Washi* and we can see at each production center several persons taking training courses. They are enjoying boiling and softening of the raw material and making paper which is a heart-warming sight, making the surroundings cheerful.

However, after 2 or 3 months of training most of them leave but to learn the whole process of *Washi*, the term is too short.

At first sight, it may seem that the papermaker is only simply shaking the papermaking mold forward and sideways but it is necessary to spread the pulp stock water over all the screen and to intertwine the fibers as much as possible. For that reason, the pulp stock water must be moved around vigorously. We have heard from persons engaged in papermaking for 40-50 years that "papermaking is difficult".

Again, paper requiring a very thin caliper or special homogenity, is very difficult to make. Recently, different types of *Washi* have increased i. e. difference of raw materials and quality, difference in size, thickness and sheet formation, so learning papermaking according to the end use becomes necessary.

Anyone can make paper

Drying of *Washi* is also difficult, so measures must be taken so that wrinkles do not appear, so the surface of paper touching the dryer surface will not become fluffy and for that, checking of the dryer surface and application of the brush must be studied so that wrinkles do not appear due to uneven heat in the dryer.

Making a homogenous sheet or drying without damaging the paper is more difficult than imagined and a long term for learning the technique is necessary.

Answer : **Kenichi Miyazaki**

Washi Training Centers		
Kayabuki no Yado	945-15 Kadoide Takayanagi-cho, Kariwa-gun, Niigata Pref.	Tel. 0257-41-2361
Kazuo Ito	959-44 2689 Koide Kawakami Mura, Higashi Kambara-gun, Niigata Pref.	Tel. 02549-5-2920
Gokagami Kyodo Kumiai	939-19 Shimonashi Tairamura Higashi Tonami-gun, Toyama Pref.	Tel. 0763-66-2016
Tairamura Washi Kogei Kenkyukan	939-19 223 Higashi Nakae Tairamura, Higashi Tonami-gun Toyama Pref.	Tel. 0763-66-2223
Keijusha Washi Bunko	939-23 668-4 Kagami-machi Yatsuo-cho, Nei-gun, Toyama Pref.	Tel. 0764-55-1184
Papyrus Kan	915-02 Shinzaike Imadate-cho, Imadate-gun, Fukui Pref.	Tel. 0778-42-1363
Eishiro Abe Kinenkan	690-21 1754 Higashi Iwasaka, Yagumo Mura, Yatsuka-gun, Shimane Pref.	Tel. 0852-54-1745
Awa Tesukiwashi Shokogyo Kaikan	779-34 136 Kawahigashi Yamakawa-cho, Oe-gun, Tokushima Pref.	Tel. 0883-42-2772
Ohzu Washi Kaikan	795-03 Ooaza Hiraoka, Ikazaki-cho, Kita-gun, Ehime Pref.	Tel. 0893-44-2002
Inomachi Kami no Hakubutsukan	761-21 110-0 Saiwai-cho, Inomachi, Agawa-gun, Kochi Pref.	Tel. 0888-93-0886
Karasuyama Washi Kaikan	321-06 6-8-2 chome, Chuo, Karasuyama-cho, Nasu-gun, Tochigi Pref.	Tel. 02878-2-2100

Anybody may experience papermaking. Please make prior appointment by phone before visiting.

What are the climate conditions necessary for papermaking?

When visiting *Washi* producing areas away from the city, it seems we have returned to an older age.

When entering *Washi* producing areas nestled between mountains, a pleasant breeze blows, the sound of water in making paper and the sound of beating raw material can be heard. Also, in the sweet smell of boiling *Kozo* and in the rising smoke, the scent of tradition can be experienced.

In the structure of the traditional house, most of the rooms are arranged so that the living area and working area are placed together and the papermaking area is set in the best place, facing south. *Washi* produced by sheets must not be uneven in thickness. For that reason, it is necessary to work in a bright, sunny spot. Also, at the raw material preparation area, in order to prevent the outbreak of decomposing bacteria and for storage of *Neri* to prevent deterioration of viscosity of *Tororo-aoi* mucilage, a dark interior area where temperature does not rise so highly even in summer, is selected. In this way, for the papermaking area, an environment well ventilated and with minimum temperature change is appreciated.

Also, *Washi* producing areas are always located near large rivers where water is plentiful. Even in production areas where there no neighboring rivers, they utilize the melted snow flow, water from mountain streams or subterranian water.

Washi requires a great amount of water. To produce a ton of paper, 1500-2000 tons of water is consumed so an abundant water source is necessary. For reference, in case of western-style papers, the amount of water consumed is only 1/10th of *Washi* consumption.

Water quality is also important in making *Washi*. The late Ichibei Iwano who was designated a living national treasure would, when visiting a papermaking area, taste the water and say "This water tastes good. It has the optimum conditions for papermaking".

Of course, muddy water, water containing a great amount of calcium carbonate or magnesium carbonate or containing iron (chalybeate water) cannot be used. It is because calcium carbonate and magnesium carbonate have the chemical action of counteracting the *Neri* function. (cf. Question 13). Water with much ferrous content makes the bleaching of the raw material difficult and after a few years, brown specks (oxidation) appear on the surface of of the paper. That such specks should appear on the precious finished production will make it worthless.

Answer : **Kenichi Miyazaki**

Kurodani village, Kyoto

How is the front surface and back surface of paper formed?

Generally, the smooth surface is the face and the rough surface is the back. According to the paper, the difference between the face and the back is either pronounced or small. To find the reason how the face and back of a paper is formed, let us review the papermaking process.

When the fiber dispersed water is scooped up onto the screen, only the fibers are caught on the screen and the water flows away downward. The ply of the fiber left on the screen becomes paper.

Long and short fibers are both dispersed in the water but when the fibers are caught on the ribs of the screen, first, the long fibers are caught and the short fibers slip through the ribs and flow down into the water. Next, as the long fibers are caught on the screen, the rib space becomes narrower and the short fibers are caught.

In this way, the fibers are piled up so when observing the cross section of the finished paper, the side of paper in contact with the screen has more long fibers and the other side not touching the screen, many short fibers are mixed with the long fibers. When long fibers are in abundance, unevenness of the surface is prominent and when short fibers are plentiful, the surface seems to be smooth. This is the first reason the front and back surface of a paper is formed.

The second reason can be found in the drying sector. Paper with moisture removed still contains much moisture so it is spread on a wooden board or on the metal plate of a dryer. The moisture

content is evaporated by the radiant solar heat or the conductive heat of steam.

When spreading on a wooden board or metal plate, a brush is used to spread out the wet sheet and some traces of the brush remain but the surface of one side is pressed upon the surface of the board so it will become smooth. *Washi* dryed on wooden boards are often seen to have the grain of the board imprinted on it. Anyway, the smooth surface touching the board is the face and the side which has the brush traces is the back.

This is more conspicous when paper is dryed on a steel dryer and as the moisture between the fiber evaporates and when the fibers become more and more interlock-ed, the fibers are drawn to one direction on the surface of the dryer so unevenness which is caused by the thickness of the fiber becomes more prominent on the surface of the side not touching the plate.

In order to prevent this second cause, in the case of "*Kyokushi*" (durable printing paper, cf. Glossary), the paper is spread upon a wooden frame and dryed. Therefore, there will be no brush traces and a paper with both sides smooth is made. However, the first cause is not completely eliminated so strictly speaking, the front surface and back surface of the paper remain.

Answer : **Akinori Ohkawa**

How is a watermark made?

A design visible when looking through paper is called a "watermark". The thin part of the paper is bright and the thick part looks dark. A design made only by the thin part of the paper is called "white watermark" and the design utilizing the thin and thick part is called "black watermark".

The 1,000 yen and 10,000 yen notes issued by the Bank of Japan have the "black watermark". According to the law, "black watermark" cannot be used unless special permission is given so the watermark used in general writing and book papers are all "white watermarks".

It is said watermark designs began in the 12th century in Europe and there is also an example of watermarks being used in feu-

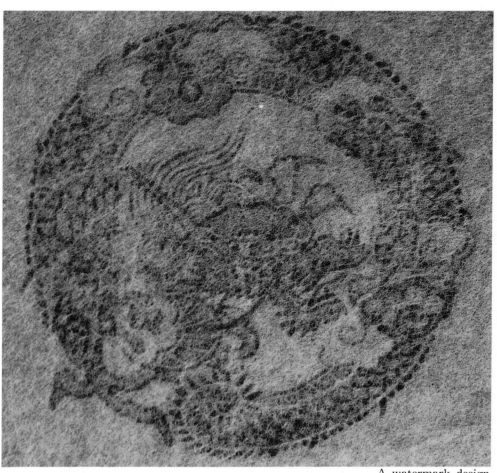

A watermark design

dal government notes during the *Yedo* period. (1603-1867)

By placing wire bent in design form on the screen and then making paper, the paper becomes thin at the wire part so when it is held to the light, it looks bright and white against the background. This is called "white watermark".

In case of a flexible bamboo screen, such hard material as wire cannot be used so *Shibugami* (a thick strong paper treated with persimmon tannin) is cut into the form of a design and sewed onto the screen. The rib which makes the screen and the impression of the thread with which the ribs are wove looks white and these are called "rib marks" or "thread marks" not watermarks. However, in principle, they may be called a kind of "white watermark".

To make "black watermarks" put the indentation in a fine mesh wire and use it instead of a screen, then make paper. In the depressed part of the indent, the paper gets thick and the projecting areas become thinner. Therefore, a person's face and other designs can be freely expressed.

Generally, watermarks come out clearly if the fiber is short so in *Washi* using long fibered *Kozo*, a clear watermark will not appear. "Rib marks" and "thread marks" are also not clear for that reason. Therefore, when making watermarks in "*Hosho*" (cf. Glossary) and other papers, the lines of the design are made a little broader and a clear "white watermark" is formed.

Watermarks are not only made in *Washi* but many watermarks are made on machine-made papers. The method of making watermarks differs from that of handmade papers. After fibers are caught on the wire screen, a round roll with a watermark is pressed upon the fiber ply. The fibers are pushed away by the relief and becomes thin, causing a watermark.

Answer : **Akinori Ohkawa**

What kind of material is used to impart color to Washi? The method?

This can be largely divided into dyes and pigments. By dye, the component having color, in other words, the coloring dissolves in water and with a certain force, remains in between the fibers or permeates the interior of the fiber itself minutely and imparts color.

In case of pigments, they do not dissolve in water, but minute corpuscles of pigment color the fiber by using a binding agent.

Dyes can be divided into natural dyes and synthetic dyes. There are vegetable and animal dyes in natural dyes and the representative animal dyes are shell purple and cochineal. After steeping shell purple in a liquid secreted by a kind of snail shell, it gives off a beautiful purple color by oxidization. Cochineal is a scale parasite living on cactus of Central and South America and after steaming the male, it is dried. Shell purple is used by itself but cochineal needs a mordant to help the dye settle and ferric oxide rouge (imparts red color) or alum (imparts reddish purple color) is necessary.

Vegetable dyes are diversified and dyes are extracted from various parts of the vegetable i. e. root, tree trunk, bark, stem leaf, flower bud, fruit, etc. . Aside from

Synthetic dyes

Natural dyes

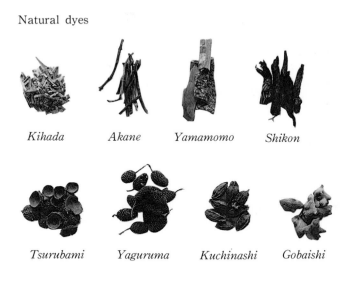

Kihada   Akane   Yamamomo   Shikon

Tsurubami   Yaguruma   Kuchinashi   Gobaishi

Kihada (Phellodedron amurense) tree bark and some other vegetable dyes, a mordant is necessary and according to the mordant, the color changes.

Regarding synthetic dyes, a British chemist by the name of W. H. Perkin was synthesizing a specific chemical to find a way to treat malaria and he unexpectedly discovered the basic dyestuff "Mauvein" which is said to be the first synthetic dye.

Later, many colors were discovered and were easily obtainable, so are widely used. Most of them are direct dyes and light colors stay fixed comparatively easy. However, as the color becomes deeper, fixing of the color is difficult and a mordant or fixative such as alum or alum cake is necessary.

Regarding pigments, there are inorganic pigments such as finely ground minerals and shells and organic pigments extracted from animals or synthesized from petroleum. At present, it may be said that almost everything surrounding us is colored by pigments. They have varigated colors and compared to dyes, they do not discolor when exposed to heat or light. However, it is also true that when dyeing by pigments, sometimes a binding agent is necessary and as it does not dissolve in water, it is difficult to handle.

These dyes and pigments are used to dye *Washi* and one method is to dye the pulp stock and then make paper and the other method is to dye the paper after it is made. The first is called pre-dye and the latter, after-dye.

In case of after-dye, the most general method is brushing by which the dye or pigment is brushed onto the surface of the paper. By brushing several colors on a wet sheet, the boundry between the colors become blurred and an elegant dyed paper can be made.

Other methods, i.e. blurring the colors by using a spray or folding up the paper into triangles or squares and dipping the corners or sides in different colored dye liquid which creates pleasant designs when opened is called *Orizome* (fold dyeing). In all, there are many types of dyeing methods.

Answer : **Akinori Ohkawa**

Why are there blurring and non-blurring papers?

Paper is formed by many fibers intertwined with each other and is porous with countless openings between the fibers. If a drop of water is dropped on the paper, it will immediately be absorbed and this is due to the quality of adaptability to water of the fibers and capillary action.

The first reason for the difference of blurring in papers that can be considered is the raw material. Using fibers which have thick film (membrane) as hemp, a porous paper will be made and water absorption will be great. On the other hand, thin film fiber as *Gampi* is not so porous and water absorption decreases.

Again, using the same fibers, if beating is increased, the fiber will become soft and intertwining between fibers will increase so openings will decrease and the degree of blurring will become smaller.

The second reason that can be considered is the chemicals used during the process of making *Washi*. Especially, the chemicals used in the boiling process not only greatly influences paper strength but also water absorption and blurring. When using such weak alkali agents as wood ash and sodium carbonate, much non-fibrous matter remains between the fibers and increases binding between the fibers and decreases the number of openings. Therefore, the paper will become somewhat hard and blurring will be less.

When boiling by such strong alkali agents as caustic soda with an eye to higher bleaching, oppositely, the more bleaching increases, the more non-fibrous matter is dissolved so the paper becomes more pourous and much blurring will occur.

When writing on *Washi*, it blurs greatly. Therefore according to the end use of *Washi*, as a method to prevent blurring, sizing is carried out.

The method of carrying out sizing on the surface of paper is called surface sizing and by clogging the openings in the interior of the paper by a sizing agent and preventing water penetration is called interior sizing.

Besides glue, rosin and starch, synthetic resin, etc. are used for sizing. The representative surface sizing method is called *"Dosa"* application which is to brush a liquid mixed with glue and alum on the paper. In the paper using this method, blurring stops and is used for such papers as *"Kana Shodoyoshi"* (Japanese phonetic character calligraphy paper), Japanese painting paper and special printing papers.

The representative method of adding sizing agent to the pulp stock prior to making paper to restrain blurring is called rosin sizing. Rosin is added while stirring the pulp stock and then, aluminium sulphate is added to fix the rosin on the fiber. However, recently, using aluminium sulphate as a fixing is the cause of deterioration of paper so instead, a method using neutral or weak alkali sizing has been adopted.

Answer : **Akinori Ohkawa**

Why is Washi prone to be fluffy? What method is there to prevent it?

When erasing a pencil mistake from the surface of *Washi*, the fibers become twisted and the surface becomes fluffy which gives it an untidy look. Again, when printing on *Washi*, after a short time, fibers are picked from the paper by the printing ink. These fibers cling to the printing plate and make printing impossible.

In case of western-style paper, erasures or in printing, there is no trouble. Though using the same wood pulp, paper made by only dispersing the wood pulp in water is weak and becomes a paper prone to be fluffy, the same as *Washi*. In other words, paper is made by cohesion between fibers so in case of non-treated fibers, strong cohesion between fibers does not take place.

Since old times, it is said that "paper is made by beating" so in the process of making paper, beating is a very important mechanical treating process as this process gives that paper a wide breadth of variation.

The main function of beating is to bruise the wall surrounding the fiber and allow water to permeate the interior of the fiber and cause expansion and by that action to make the fibril loosen from the fiber itself. The beaten fibers contact with each other nicely and as a result, the cohesion area enlarges, openings between fibers decrease resulting in a high density, compact sheet.

Paper using wood pulp can be made into various kinds of paper according to the degree of beating from such soft papers as tissues to

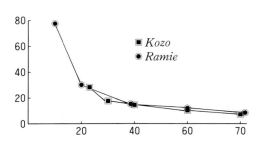

Water absorption
mm/5min.

Beating degree (Schopper/Riegler)

printing paper, wrapping paper, etc..

In the process of making *Washi*, there is the same beating stage but the object is to dissolve the bundles of fiber one by one by agitating the pulp and is somewhat different from the beating of western-style papers. A nicely formed, pliant, tear-resistant paper can be made without beating the raw materials for *Washi* i.e. *Kozo*, *Mitsumata* and *Gampi*, but fluffiness is apt to happen.

In order to reduce fluffiness, by using a weak alkali boiling agent such as wood ash and sodium carbonate, it is necessary to let more non-fiberous matter remain or increase the beating time. Another method is to apply glue, starch, casein or synthetic resin to make a film on the surface which increases cohesion of fibers more strongly so fluffiness can be controlled more.

Answer : **Akinori Ohkawa**

Fluffiness

Question 26.

How can bookworms or stains be prevented?

When opening an old book, there are some that are full of bookworm holes. Also, when books are piled on top of each other near a wall, there are times when the back cover is eaten by bookworms and crumbles into pieces.

There are several kinds of bookworms and the following four are the ones that especially cause most damage.

Yamato Shimi (Yamato bookworm). Most generally seen and there is a tendency of more individual count in warmer areas. In Japan, they are called *Shimi* (bookworm), *Kiramushi* (silverfish) or *Hakumushi* (leafworms) and are known as harmful insects for *Washi* and other material. They exist mostly in libraries and pasted Washi papers.

Gokiburi (cockroach). This is the main harmful insect of the

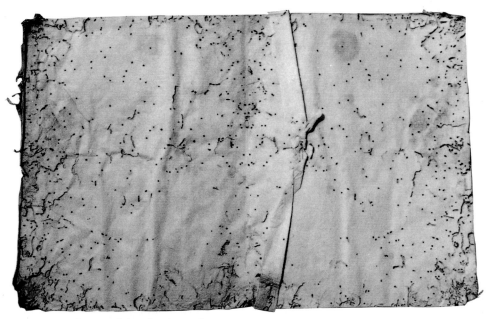

Kozo paper damaged by deathwatch

household and *Yamato Gokiburi* (Japanese cockroach) and *Kuro Gokiburi* (black cockroach) are known from old times. The same as *Shimi*, they prefer the pasted part of *Washi* papers and especially damage back covers of books.

Shibanmushi (deathwatch). A small size beetle about 3 millimeters, famous as harmful insects of second-hand books. They do not damage the pasted part of the book as the *Shimi* but damage the book by making tunnel holes.

Shiroari (white ants, termites). A famous harmful insect which almost everybody knows. *Shiroari* and *Japanese Shiroari* cause damage to houses and wooden structures. They do not attack books from the beginning but migrate from structures. These insects prefer dark and damp places so to store books, a sunny, well ventilated place is important. Regarding books which have already been worm eaten, they should be left in a well ventilated place and dried in the shade. After repelling the ants, they should be stored together with an insectide. For an insectide, clothing-use naphtalene or paradichloro benzine will do.

Next, regarding stains on the paper, it is annoying to see brown stains appearing here and there on valuable pasted scroll paintings or paper tablets. 2 reasons can be given.

One is due to the steel plate used during drying of the wet sheet. The wet sheet is brushed onto the steel plate and heat-dried and at that time, a small amount of ferrous material is transfered to the paper. After a long period of time, that ferrous material becomes oxidized and appears as a stain. Now, use of steel plates has been abolished and changed to stainless steel plates so this problem is being solved.

The other cause is due to microbes. Those contained in the raw material and those in the atmosphere which attach themselves to the paper. After adequate heat and humidity is provided and the conditions are proper, the microbes start to become active and cocoon spinoffs (threads) appear and cocoon roots generate organic acid and that part becomes the cause of brown spots.

In order to protect valuable and precious documents from these stains, it is important to do as much as possible so that dust does not adhere to the the paper and to protect it from humidity.

Answer : **Kou Hamada**

Question 27.

What kind of tools are used for Washi?

Washi is made by using a tool called *Sugeta* (papermaking mold, cf. Glossary). The *Sugeta* is a screen using bamboo or miscanthus (Japanese pampas grass, miscanthus sinensis) ribs woven with silk threads which is placed in a wooden frame.

Bamboo ribs are made by using black bamboo (Phyllostachys puberilla) or long jointed bamboo (Phyllostachys bambusoides). The ones cut in October or November are the best and these ribs are woven together for the bamboo screen. It is necessary to have the length of the bamboo rib over 40 cms so the longer the length between the joints are, the better it is and from one stalk of bamboo only 7 or 8 sections can be used. The bamboo is finely split and the outer bark and the pith removed and are made into one rib each. To weave one screen 2 ft × 3 ft (about 60×90 cm), generally 2000 ribs are necessary. According to the type of *Washi*, the diameter of the ribs differ ranging from 0.5 to 0.7 millimeter.

The material for miscanthus ribs is miscanthus which is gathered in autumn just before the frost comes and slender head stems are selected. Usable dried and selected ribs are only about one third of the amount gathered.

Miscanthus screen is used in making *Washi* for mounting and calligraphy.

The thread which is used to weave the screen is a strong silk thread tanned with persimmon tannin. Of course, the count of the thread changes with the size of the rib. The count of the thread is indicated by the weight of three threads, 49 meters long. Thread for *Shojigami* screen use is 3 momme 2 bu (about 12 gms).

Screen weaving is done by pairs of threads which are looped around the ribs in a chain line at regular intervals. In order to keep the tightness even, the threads are wound on bobbins of even weight.

It takes about a week to weave one screen. The final finishing is done by dipping the screen in water and then deciding the size of the screen to fit the frame.

The frame is made of straight-grained high grade *Hinoki* (Japanese ground cypress) which has been dried for some time and which has no warp. The frame is made slightly convex so that when the pulp stock is scooped up into the frame, the weight of that stock will level it out.

As metal fittings for the frame are used in water, bronze is used as it is rust-resistant and has a certain degree of elasticity which is necessary. From a bronze rod, fixtures such as hasps, handles, etc. are made and from bronze wire, blunt supporting pins are made. All are made by hand.

In this way, it is important to select light and strong wood material which is stable whether wet or dry.

Answer : **Kenichi Miyazaki**

Metal screen for *Tamezuki*

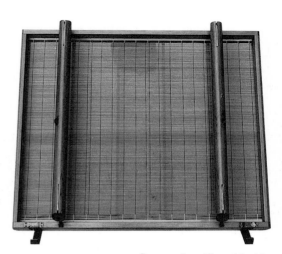

Screen for *Nagashizuki*

How many people are there currently who make equipment for Washi? How about their successors?

E quipment making can be broken down into makers of bamboo ribs, miscanthus ribs, weaving threads, screen weaving, frames, metal fixtures, brushes, metal patterns and watermarks.

In old times, there were many papermakers so equipment making craftsmen were in control of their special department and devoted themselves to their work but in recent years, the number of papermakers have decreased greatly so demand for equipment has also decreased. Now there are only 30 equipment makers throughout Japan and almost all of them are aged and have no successor. However, they still continue equipment making but in a very scaled down condition.

Considering this situation, in 1974, the National Washi Equipment Preservation Society was established and such matters as technical interchange, exchange of information and successor training measures were taken up to be studied. The government, in 1976, in order to preserve the equipment maker's technique which supports the *Washi* industry, designated this society as a Cultural Properties Protection Technique Preservation Organization and is stressing the inheritance of that technique.

Most of the members of the society live in Kochi where *Tosa Washi* is produced and there are makers of bamboo ribs, miscanthus ribs, weaving thread, screen frames, metal fixtures and brushes who take orders not only from local *Washi* makers but also from *Washi* makers throughout Japan.

In Gifu were *Mino Washi* is produced, there are 4 makers of screen frames, metal fixtures and brushes and in Fukui where *Echizen Washi* is produced, due to the relation to more design-oriented *Washi*, there are 7 makers of metal patterns, watermarks and screen frames who protect tradi-

Splitting bamboo

tional know-how and technique, centering their trade to the local demand.

In other areas, such as Ehime and Tottori where *Washi* is produced, screen frame makers make equipment for calligraphy paper and in Shizuoka, 2 screen frame makers taking orders from *Washi* makers in neighboring Yamanashi. Especially, in this area, there are orders for screens for machine-made *Washi* and a long screen with a width of 1 meter and length of 10 meters is made every now and then, taking a month to manufacture.

Regarding the problem of successors to equipment makers, recently young Yoshiro Kinuyama (born 1957) from Saitama decided to follow the trade and presently has started screen weaving and frame making studies at Ino-cho, Kochi. He has already studied *Washi* making for 5 years and made this decision undaunted by the current situation of screen frame making. Noboru Inoue (born 1906)who has spent all his life making screen frames for *Tosa Tengujo*, replied to his intentions and is teaching him earnestly. Currently, his studies have advanced to the stage where he is able to take orders for small-size equipment.

For *Washi* makers, this is good news and everybody is looking forward to his independence.

Answer : **Kenichi Miyazaki**

Finished bamboo ribs

Washi Making Process

Process	KOZO White Bark	KOZO 60%	KOZO 60%	KOZO Black Bark	MITSUMATA White Bark	MITSUMATA Black Bark	GAMPI	GAMPI
1 Boiling (1)	Soda Ash or Slaked Lime	Soda Ash or Slaked Lime	Caustic Soda	Caustic Soda	Soda Ash or Slaked Lime	Caustic Soda	Soda Ash or Slaked Lime	Caustic Soda
2 Water Rinsing	O	O	O	O	O	O	O	O
3 Bleaching — Natural	O	O			O			
3 Bleaching — Chlorine			O	O		O		O
4 Water Rinsing			O	O		O		O
5 Speck Removal (2)	O	O			O		O	
6 Beating	O	O	O	O			O	
7 Fiber Dissolving (3) — Naginata or Hollander Beater	O	O	O	O				
7 Fiber Dissolving (3) — Hollander Beater					O	O	O	O
8 Screening (Speck removal)					O		O	
9 Papermaking (4)	O	O	O	O	O	O	O	O
10 Pressing	O	O	O	O	O	O	O	O
11 Drying (5)	O	O	O	O	O	O	O	O
12 Finishing	O	O	O	O	O	O	O	O

(1) Whatever kind of chemical is used, boil 2-4 hours after water reaches boiling point.

(2) Speck removal: wet and dry removal once each.

(3) For Kozo fiber dissolving, either Naginata or Hollander beater is used but the Naginata beater is better for the fiber.

(4) For papermaking, either bamboo screen, miscanthus screen or silk gauze is used.

(5) For drying, drying board or triangular dryer is used.

Depending on the raw materials, there are processing differences indicated by O marks.

WASHI
ORIGIN AND
PRESENT SITUATION

29. When and where was paper invented?
30. When was Washi originally made?
31. Tell us more about the history of Washi.

Japanese kite

When and where was paper invented?

It was long believed that Ts'ai Lun of China invented paper. It originated from the *"Gokansho"* (history of the Latter Han Dynasty) which describes that Ts'ai Lun who was head of the government department making utensils used by the court, made paper in 105 using wood bark, jute fiber, rags and macerated fish nets probably made from jute cord. The people called this *Ts'ai Koshi* (distinguished Ts'ai Lun's paper).

However, recently, from remains of the Former Han Dynasty (207BC-9AD) in China, actual paper was unearthed and the origin of paper is being restudied. These papers are jute papers and jute fiber and crushed pieces of jute cloth are mixed in it.

Mankind has devised many ways to find material to inscribe letters. Pressing letters on clay then baking them into bricks, casting it in metal, inscribing letters on stone or bones, using animal hides such as sheepskin, using vegetation such as tapa of tree barks or papyrus varies with the purpose of leaving such writings or according to the natural environment.

In ancient China, besides paper, such material as wood or bamboo tablets, silk cloth or hemp cloth, etc., all which have strong and weak points were used for writing and copy material. From the excavations of the Ma-Wang-Tui Han tomb of the Former Han Dynasty (207BC-9AD), a silk cloth with original Lao-Tzu (Chinese philosopher, born 604BC, founder of Taoism) teachings written on it has been found and at that time,

Papyrus

precious documents and drawings were written on elaborate cloth and it seems that paper was regarded as low grade writing or copy material. Technology developed and the many strong points of paper, it's handiness, weight, surface beauty, writability, strength, long storage life, as well as the availablity of abundant raw materials with which to make paper, raised its status for use as a writing material for important high grade documents of the court. Ts'ai Lun was probably the reforming innovator of paper technique.

As mentioned before, Former Han Dynasty paper was excavated from such important places of the Silk Road as Kansu and Sinkiang and this indicates that paper was, from an early age, found to be serviceable in Central Asian countries.

During the Tang dynasty (618-906), the Islam world expanded rapidly and ruled the area from the Iberian peninsula to Iran and flourished both economically and culturally. In 751, the Tang dynasty warred with Islam and lost on the banks of the Tarus river and at that time, paper artisans were captured as prisoners of war and papermaking spread to the Islam world. Later, from the 8th to 11th century, paper named after production centers such as Samarkand, Bagdad, Damascus was exported to Europe and other countries of the world. During the 8th century when Spain was ruled by Islam, a paper mill was erected, and in the 12th century, papermaking spread to France. Papermaking spread to Italy via Damascus and in the 14th century, production was flourishing, contributing to the Renaissance culture. Later, papermaking gradually spread to other European countries.

Answer : **Shin Yagihashi**

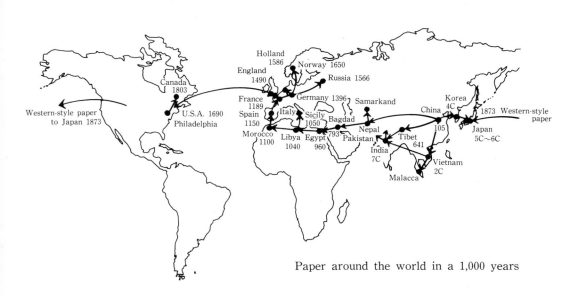

Paper around the world in a 1,000 years

When was Washi originally made?

Paper invented in China spread immediately to Asian countries.

For instance, at the end of the 2nd century, a prototype of paper was introduced to Viet Nam and in the Wei, Chin and South and North Dynasty period (386-617) papermaking started. In 641, a noblewoman from the Tang (618-690) court married a noble in Tibet and brought paper, India ink and brush artisans along with her. During the Han Dynasty, China had trade with India and before the end of the 7th century, papermaking began there and spread to Nepal, Pakistan and Malacca. Papermaking spread to Korea from early times and it is said it started in the 4th century.

In Japan, paper was known through Buddhism (officially introduced in 548) to be convenient and the oldest article mentioning papermaking was written in the *Nihon Shoki* (The Chronicles of Japan, 30 volumes, completed 720) concerning the 18th year of the reign of Empress Suiko (610) where it says "The King of Korea and priest *Doncho* presented Buddhist sutras. *Doncho* is well versed in Buddhist scriptures and skillfully makes pigments, paper and India ink. He also introduced a

The million pagoda Dharani (oldest printed matter in Japan)

water powered mortar. This must be the first time in history that such a water powered mortar was made."

However, considering the fact that many craftsmen came from Korea and the circumstances that Japan required paper, and on the other hand, that there is no poem on paper in the *"Manyou-shu"* (The oldest collection of poems, 20 volumes, around 4500 poems, present form completed around 750) which describes the life of common people, it can be assumed that in a period not far from the reign of Empress Suiko (592-628), immigrant craftsmen from the Korean peninsula started papermaking.

35 years after Priest *Doncho* arrived in Japan, Law Reformation of the *Taika* age (646) took place and it stipulated that family registration be started. 60 years later, the *Kogo Nenjaku* (670) which was a family register of a national scale was enforced and 80 years later, the *Koin Nenjaku* (690) which was a family register revised every 6 years was completed and with this as a basis, the law of farmland distribution was promulgated.

Reviewing the expansion of demand for official document papers under these circumstances, *Doncho*'s achievement was in introducing the newest method of high productivity papermaking. In this meaning, the mortar utilizing water power is related not only to papermaking but also to making of pigments and India ink and especially in papermaking, crushing of hemp rags and helping in producing uniform quality raw material in volume.

In identification of age, the oldest remaining actual examples of *Washi* are the Mino (Gifu) Chikuzen (Fukuoka) and Buzen (between Fukuoka and Oita) family register paper of the 2nd year of *Taiho* (702) stored in *Shoso-In* in Nara. They are *Kozo* paper made in each area and not only demonstrate the technical standard of each area but it is also interesting in that the present characteristics of *Kozo* of each area can be seen such as the Kyushu *Kozo* having red streaks mixed and *Mino Kozo* having a gentle paper surface.

Recently excavated lacquered paper writings (waste paper used for the paper lid of lacquered buckets) were also found to be such official documents as family registers or government loan certificates so this demonstrates the huge paper demand of those times.

Answer : **Shin Yagihashi**

Question 31.

Tell us more about the history of Washi.

The long history of *Washi* over a thousand and several hundred years can be roughly divided into two periods. The first period continues up to the end of the *Heian* period (end of the 12th century) from around the end of the 5th century when the papermaking technique was introduced to Japan. The latter period is from the *Kamakura* period (1192-1333) up to the present.

The first half is a period when Japan was controlled by a bureaucratic structure called *Ritsuryo* (laws amd regulations) system modeled on the Chinese example. As it was a well-organized structure, a massive amount of paper was necessary for government use connecting the central and local offices and for family register paper which was the basis for taxation or conscription of soldiers (an original and 2 copies were kept by the central and local government offices). At the capital, a government sponsored new papermaking mill called *Shioku-In* (cf. Note) was established which made paper for court requirements such as calligraphy paper which was elaborately and beauti-

fully decorated. *Shioku-In* also had an important role in teaching papermaking in the local areas but production at the mill itself was small. Paper for correspondence sent to the central government from the local offices was, in principle, the responsibilty of local authorities so papermaking techniques spread quickly throughout the country.

Among items still remaining and kept in *Shoso-In* are family registers sent to the central government from all areas of Japan. The date of some registers can be definitely confirmed and among them, there are papers from Mino (Gifu), Chikuzen (Fukuoka) and Buzen (between Fukuoka and Oita). These registers are dated 702 and are regarded as the oldest examples of *Washi* remaining. The technical standard of these papers vary but it is interesting to notice the local standard of each district and how the paper compares with current *Washi* products from the area.

Investigation of papers stored in *Shoso-In* shows that the representative *Washi* of the ancient times were hemp, *Gampi* and *Kozo* papers and especially hemp was highly esteemed as it had a long history in China. For the highest class correspondence, hemp papers were used. Also, there were many cases where *Gampi* and *Kozo* fibers were mixed together with hemp.

Holding examples of *Washi* made from the *Nara* period (710-794) to the *Heian* period (794-1192) to light, the fiber direction is scattered and unsettled (characteristic of *Tamezuki*) in most examples of this time, but the direction of fibers began to become uniform vertically so *Nagashizuki* sheet formation which is the characteristic of *Washi*, is thought to have been developed during the *Heian* period. The use of *Neri* is necessary for *Nagashizuki* and initially, it is said that *Gampi* mixed with *Kozo* was the origin of the idea to use *Neri*.

During the *Heian* period (794-1192), *Washi* making technique developed further. When using hemp, the long fiber must be cut so it was necessary to cut it each time to several millimeters or beat it in a mortar. The surface of the finished hemp paper was rough so such treatment as pounding or polishing was necessary. On the other hand, *Kozo* fiber was about 1 centimeter and was most appropriate for papermaking as the fibers interlocked easily to form a strong paper. *Gampi* fibers were also about 3 millimeter and semi-transparent so when made into papers, the texture was so very fine that the color beneath could be seen. Therefore, vegetable-dyed thin papers could be placed upon each other and a neutral tint could be obtained. Japanese poems composed of 31 syllables were written on this paper.

Due to difficulties of raw material preparation and the rough texture, manufacture of hemp paper deteriorated and *Kozo* and *Gampi* papers became the key papers of Washi. Cultivation of *Kozo* was easy and as it could be grown in all places throughout Japan, *Kozo* paper accounted for more than half of the total *Washi* production. On the other hand, *Gampi* could not be cultivated and only natural stands could be collected so production was limited but *Gampi* paper was favored as a special high-grade paper.

The compilation of these new techniques of *Washi* is the Japanese phonetic character calligraphy paper used in the "*Nishi Honganjibon Sanjurokunin Kashu*" (volume of the selected poems of 36 outstanding poets) collected in the middle of the *Heian* period (794-1192) and now in possession of the *Nishi Honganji* (Head temple of the *Nishi Honganji* sect). This can be said to illustrate the apex of nobility culture in Japan.

With the fall of the bureaucratic structure built upon the *Ritsuryo* system and nobility and after the *Kamakura* period (1192-1333) when the *Bushi* (samurai) class appeared, *Washi* began to be produced in a new environment. *Washi* was not required to be supplied as a form of tax from the local villages but was sent to the capital as merchandise. In the local areas and in the capital, a market for paper and raw material, *Kozo*, was established and traders transported these items and gained a profit. The paper which won popularity at these markets became known throughout Japan. For instance, *Sugiharashi* (The name of the paper and place of production are the same) originated from a local area in Hyogo Pref. and became a paper representative of the middle ages. A set of *Sugiharashi* and a fan was called "*Issoku*

Ippon" (10 quire of paper and a fan) and was extensively used as a gift from priests and samurai on a formal visit or on congratulatory occasions.

Many of the feudal clans during the *Yedo* period (1603-1867) monopolized *Washi* production within their territory and sent it to the central markets of Osaka or Yedo (Tokyo). With this profit, they took measures to manage the financial affairs of the clan (paper monopoly system). It was due to the great increase in demand for paper during the *Yedo* period. By the *Nagashizuki* method of production, *Washi* came to possess such characteristics as thinness, strength and beauty. Therefore, besides being a vehicle for writing, a broader use for *Washi* that included all parts of daily life such as food, clothing and shelter was developed.

At that time, papermaking developed into a representative industry in Japan. Paper representing the *Yedo* period were *Echizen Hosho* (Fukui), *Naoshi of Mino* (Gifu), *Nishinouchishi* (Ibaragi) and *Hodomurashi* (Tochigi) which are all famous and are still being made at present.

Due to the *Meiji* Restoration (1867), *Washi* faced a great turning point as it lost the support of their clans. However, work increased for the papermakers. The reason is that Japan suddenly rushed into a capitalistic society without ample preparation of the conditions, so it was necessary for the papermakers to sustain paper demand which increased tremendously. According to government statistics, the number of papermakers increased each year and in 1901, it reached a high of 68,562 but later decreased gradually. A western-style paper mill established in 1872, gradually started normal manufacture of machine-made paper from that time.

From then on, *Washi* was used by the general public for such everyday life items as:

1. *Shojigami*, umbrella paper, lantern paper, etc..

2. Industrial use papers, such as typewriter base paper (*Tengujo*) or mimeograph base paper (thin *Gampi* paper) and

3. Traditional industrial use papers, such as *Hakuuchishi* (gold foil beating paper, *Gampi* paper) and mounting paper.

At present, papers of the third category remain. In addition, such papers as *Washi* picture pasting, *Washi* flower making, sutra copy papers etc. which have strong support from a wide group of enthusiasts must be included and also paper for preservation and repair of cultural assets and paper for painting are gaining closer attention.

Note.
Shioku-In
During the Daido period (806-810) this Washi producing mill was established alongside the Shioku river in Kyoto as an annex to the Bureau of Scriptorial Matters. This mill carried on the tradition of papermaking originating from 701 when the Taiho laws and regulations were promulgated stipulating papermaking by the Bureau of Scriptorial Matters and paying of taxes by paper.

Answer : **Shin Yagihashi**

WASHI
IT'S VARIOUS USES

32. How has the use of Washi changed?
33. What kind of Washi is used for industrial arts?
34. How is Washi used in repair of cultural treasures?
35. What kind of Washi is used for calligraphy?
36. What kind of Washi is used for Japanese painting?
37. Tell us about Washi and printmaking.
38. What kind of arts and crafts of Washi are there? What sort of Washi is used?
39. Tell us about Origami (paper-folding).
40. Tell us about wrapping and Washi.
41. What kind of Washi is used in mounting?
42. How is Washi used in architecture such as in houses or buildings?
43. It is said printing on Washi is difficult. Why?

Paper toy

How has the use of Washi changed?

The main use of *Washi* is a vehicle for writing and copying. As it was truly a vehicle for writing, the ancient nations strived hard to create and develop paper. But paper was not the only writing and copying material. In ancient China, silk cloth, in Europe, sheepskin were the main vehicles and a highly devoted writing and copy culture was established. Paper which was developed later, was prone to be regarded only as a mass production substitute.

In Japan, there was a period when paper and wood tablets were used together but the highest writing and copying art paper such as calligraphy paper and paper for copying of Buddhist sutras were developed on *Washi* which had just been perfected. The merger of these two movements can be said to be the primary factor for creating the world's highest grade handmade paper.

Moreover, such important qualities as thinness, smoothness, lightweight and strength are utilized in other areas besides writing.

Sliding door of the *Shoin* (study room)

For instance, among the treasures of *Shoso-In*, paper is tightly wound around the core of a brush and the core of the brocade cloth inside the mirror encasing box utilizes paper. However, during the early days of *Washi* (*Nara* period 710-784), the paper artisan probably was not aware of such use. During that age, paper was roughly divided into high grade paper for copy of Buddhist sutras and general government use paper.

Entering the perfecting period (*Nara* period 710-784), to adorn calligraphy and copying paper, such decorative techniques as *Uchikumori* (cloudy design) and *Ramonshi* (twilled design, cf. Glossary) were developed. These techniques were devised to comply with commissions for calligraphy paper by the ladies of the court who had keen artistic perception. This contributed to the birth of development of *Washi* (after the middle ages) for uses other than for calligraphy and copying.

For instance, *Fusumagami* (sliding panel paper) or *Maniaishi* (cf. Glossary) which later developed as a sliding panel printing paper are thin *Gampi* papers which contain minute particles of clay. However, this technique was born due to the fact that thin *Gampi* papers for calligraphy writing preceded this development.

As the *Shoinzukuri* (old study room style architecture) was perfected, paper for architecture such as *Shojigami* (sliding door paper) was born (cf. Glossary for *Shoinshi*). One can enjoy the orderly arrangement of fibers of the *Shojigami* used to admit light.

Yoshinogami (cf. Glossary) used to filter lacquer and oil or used as tissues and often called *Yawara* or *Yawayawa* (soft paper or softies), *Tengujo* (cf. Glossary) used for copying or to draw draft sketches are the thinnest handmade papers in the world and it is only due to the fact that *Kozo* papers are made into *Washi* by the *Nagashizuki* method that this could be accomplished.

Later, Motoori Norinaga (1730-1801) making the comparison between Japanese and Chinese paper said in his book "*Tamakatsuma*" (1793-1801, 14 vol., Essays) "Tang (China) paper can only be used for writing but besides writing, *Washi* can be used for wrapping, wiping, utensils such as boxes or baskets or twisting it into thread to tie things together. It has many uses and various qualities such as thickness, thinness, strength and softness".

That *Washi* has many end-uses somewhat resembles present day western-style papers but in the case of *Washi*, just one kind of paper can be put to various uses. From this standpoint, the outlook on the intrinsic value of *Washi*, in other words, together with paper strength such as tensile strength, firmness, texture, rattle of the paper, luster and gloss, sharpness or cloudiness brought about by the intertwining difference of fibers, etc., the ability to judge such factors with delicacy has been transmitted to posterity as traditional Japanese artistic sense.

Answer : **Shin Yagihashi**

What kind of Washi is used in industrial arts?

The most closely related industrial art sector for *Washi* is the textile dyeing industry.

Washi with *Konnyaku* (devil's tongue root) starch brushed on to it is crumpled thoroughly and then made into clothing which is called "*Kamiko*" (paper clothing). The *Konnyaku* starch keeps the *Kozo* fiber from fluffing. Even in winter, it is warm as it is wind-proof and the more it is used, it has the softness to adapt itself to the shape of the body. Such are the characteristics of this paper and the priests of *Todaiji Nigatsu-do* (temple located in Nara, completed 749) crumple the *Washi* and tailored it into vestments during the "*Omizutori* rite". (Held March 12.) The priests draw water from the well and light large pine torches which are carried to the main temple. Harbinger of Spring, the sparks of the torches bring good luck.

Shifu (paper cloth) and paper yarn

Cutting *Washi* into thin strips, twisting them into paper threads and weaving these threads make a cloth called "*Shifu*" (paper cloth). There are threads made from *Kozo* and *Gampi*. Paper thread is used for the woof while silk, cotton, hemp or paper thread is used for the warp. The more it is used, it has the pliability to adapt itself to the shape of the body and also has such characteristics as vivid color tone and the random scattering of knots which emerge when spinning paper threads into yarn. However, it must be stressed that this cloth also has strength enough to endure washing in water.

Saganishiki (Saga brocade) is a cloth which does not use *Washi* thread but is made by weaving the flat *Washi* paper itself. *Kyogami* (paper for copying Buddhist sutras) is cut into strips as in a blind, and by using a bamboo shuttle, the woof thread (paper, cotton or silk) is sent through the paper. At present, the paper for copying of Buddhist sutras is resin treated, machine-made *Mitsumata* paper but in the past, white Hoshoshi or lacquered black or brown paper or paper adorned by such decorations as gold leaf or gold dust was used. By passing the thin woof thread through the flat *Kyogami*, the delicate bumpy twill is most enjoyable so, essentially, the white *Washi* surface texture is most suitable for this cloth.

Katagami (stencil paper) is made by pasting seveal sheets of *Washi* together with persimmon tannin. The direction of the grain of each sheet is alternated to prevent expansion and contraction. A design is cut into this paper and the cut stencil is used for dyeing cloth. The design may be *Komon* (fine pattern), *Nagaita Chugata* (medium pattern) or *Kataezome* (stencil dyeing). Even though resist paste is squeezed through this stencil with a squeegee and immersed several times in water, it is still able to endure such heavy handling.

The next industrial art closely related is the lacquer art.

In order to filter lacquer, *Yoshinogami* (a thin, soft paper, cf. Glossary) is used. Thin *Kozo* and *Gampi* is used in copying the draft of the design onto the surface of the lacquerware (thin *Minogami, Tengujo*), *Gampi Hakuuchishi* (gold / silver foil beating paper) is used to make gold or silver foil and *Mitsumata Hakuaishi* (foil packaging paper) is used to preserve those foils for the gold (silver) decoration of lacquerware. Therefore, in each complicated stage of lacquer art, the role of *Washi* is highly regarded.

Also, making of the basic form for lacquered goods with *Washi* is called "Shitai" (paper core), and *Ikkanbari* and *Harinuki* are those illustrations. (cf. Note below). There are many ways of making *Shitai*, for instance, using only *Washi* or pasting *Washi* on a wooden or flax cloth core. However, in the past, lacquer coating was the main object and the basic material was unknown but currently, the tendency is to coat lacquer thinly to preserve the surface character of *Washi*. Various kinds of *Washi* are used for *Shitai* such as *Sekishu Hanshi*, *Yoshinogami*

and *Misugami* (the clay contained in the paper mixes with lacquer and becomes a suitable foundation).

Shiso Ningyo (paper doll) is made by pasting *Washi* together on a core to make a strong and brightly colored paper doll. *Minogami* and *Echizen Hosho* are used to polish and wipe the blade of the Japanese sword clean, so in various areas of industrial art, special characteristics of *Washi* are extracted and used in many ways which even the papermaker could not dream of.

Note
Ikkanbari
Washi pasted foundation coated with lacquer. Began by Ikkan Hirai, hence the name.
Harinuki
A wooden pattern pasted with Washi and after drying removing the wood pattern and coated with lacquer.

Answer : **Shin Yagihashi**

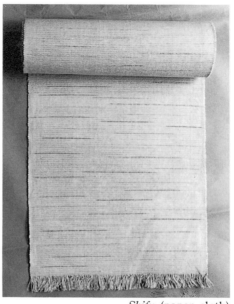

Shifu (paper cloth)

How is Washi used in repair of cultural treasures?

In order to protect paintings or manuscripts, the reason why *Washi* is often used is due to the strength of *Washi*, in other words, it is difficult to tear and endures repeated folding. However, in reality, it is the softness and stability that is utilized the most.

If only strength is considered, for several months to about 10 years, pulp paper made by machine is strong enough. However, when thinking of preservation of cultural treasures, at least a 100 years should be the target. Also, almost all cultural treasures repaired by using *Washi* are handled carefully and set gently on an appropriate pedestal away from the sun or are viewed hanging on the wall and are kept in safe-keeping. Therefore, the repairing paper does not have to be so strong. But if paper with 100% strength declines to 1/10th in strength in 10 years, it is not adequate enough but if a 30% strong paper has 20% strength left after a 100 years, that is the paper required. *Washi* meets these requirements.

Moreover, paper strength which deteriorates rapidly, often contain factors which promote deterioration or which frequently generate such factors and these factors give a bad influence directly or indirectly to cultural treasures and may well accelerate the damage.

As an illustration of *Washi* used for repair of Japanese paintings or documents, please refer to the paragraph regarding *Washi* and mounting. (cf. Question 41) I will describe how *Washi* is utilized in Europe.

At the restoration section annexed to libraries, museums and art galleries of Europe, when damages to paintings and drawings written on paper, copied documents, and woodblock printings are repaired, thin *Washi* is often used. European paper compared to *Washi* is thick and coarse so if thin *Washi* is pasted on the surface, it will not change the impression of the original paper. Also, compared to European papers, transparency of *Washi* is good so even if it is pasted on the surface of printed matter, the letters underneath will never be illegible. That is also one of the strong points of *Washi*. *Kozo* paper has transparency but *Gampi* paper is still more transparent so it is often used for repair of color printed books.

Thick *Washi* is used in places to support the page of a book. In case of European books, paper is folded in two and is sewed together with binding thread along the fold and finished but the folded part is often damaged. For that reason, *Washi* is pasted from the back surface along the fold to reinforce the page or when the fold is torn in two, at the fold. The two parts are joined together with *Washi* and the fold of *Washi* is bound. Besides being soft, even folded *Washi* is tear resistant so it is indispensible for repair of books.

When *Washi* is used for repair of oil paintings or murals, the strength of *Washi* is utilized to a certain degree. But in that case too, as it has flexibility and stability, it adapts itself to the bumps of the painted surface and it is required not to have the stability so that it does not cause any bad effects on the painted surface.

The supporting part of oil paintings is flax cloth. When the cloth ages, it is repaired by exchange of new cloth or pasting new cloth on top of the old. During the period of repair, in order to protect the painted surface, paper is pasted on the surface. Among oil paintings and murals located in art galleries or churches, *Washi* cut into long strips is pasted on the surface. When the oil paint layer is found to be starting to peel off, it must wait to be repaired so during that time in order to prevent more peeling, *Washi* is pasted on it temporarily.

Answer : **Katsuhiko Masuda**

What kind of Washi is used for calligraphy?

There are many different kinds of Washi used for calligraphy and it is important to check closely and carefully select whether the paper is to be used for Chinese characters or Japanese phonetic characters.

The many kinds of paper used for Chinese characters and Japanese phonetic characters are as follows:

Paper for Chinese characters

Hanshi (cf. Glossary) Used in general for the clean copy. Comparatively thick and blurs somewhat.

Koshugasen Made in *Koshu* (Yamanashi). Characteristics: Blurs and ink color distinct.

Inshugasen Made in *Inshu* (Tottori). Many varieties, little blurring. *Gasen* paper is also made in Fukui, Kochi and Kagawa, each area with its own characteristics.

Chugokugasen Made in *Chugoku* (China). Blurring is deep set and ink effect is good but recently, quality is deteriorating so selection must be careful.

Taiwangasen Blurring and fading is good but it seems that ink effect is not so good. Price is cheap so it is popular causing severe competition to domestic paper.

Kankokugasen (Korean). Strong quality using *Kozo* as the main raw material.

Paper for Japanese phonetic characters Differing from paper for Chinese characters, paper for this use is often decorated and the main papers are as follows:

Kakoshigasen (decorated calligraphy paper) For Japanese phonetic character use, as less blurring paper is favored *Dosa* sizing is applied. There are also papers colored by brushing on dye-stuff, spattered with gold or silver foil or decorated with printed designs. According to the density of the glue or burnt alum or due to the degree of mixing of *Gofun* (white shell powder), absorption of ink differs.

Hanshi Paper generally used is thin and smooth-surfaced. Raw material : *Mitsumata*. Paper shelved for 3 years is best for writing and seems to have a certain character.

Kumogami Literally, "cloud paper". Used for *Shikishi* (a large, square card for writing poetry) and *Tanzaku* (long strip of paper to write poems on). Colored blue on the upper part and purple on the bottom part.

Kinsenshi (*Ginsenshi*) Literally, "gold or silver embedded paper. After spreading gold or silver foil on the base paper, a thin paper (*Tengujo*) covers the foil which can be seen beneath. Used for *Shikishi* or *Tanzaku*.

Hiunshi Literally, "flying cloud paper". *Gampi* fibers which have been well beaten are dyed purple or blue and is laid on the paper in the form of a small cloud.

Suminagashishi Marbled paper. Floating India ink on water and making a design utilizing the surface tension of water which is transferred onto the paper.

Karakami A paper surfaced with white shell powder and pressed with a design mold laid with mica.

Kiritsunagishi, *Yaburitsunagishi*, *Kasanetsunagishi* Literally, "Cut-joined, tear-joined or ply-joined paper". *Karakami* and dyed papers which have been patterned by cut-joined, tear-joined or ply-joined papers.

Soshokushi Paper decorated with scattered gold or silver foil to the various forementioned papers. There are decorations of scattered gold and silver foil, gold or silver dust or gold and silver foil cut into slender strips and applied on the paper which also have designs of butterflies, birds or plants and trees using ultramarine or verdigo color.

Answer : **Etsudo Takeda**

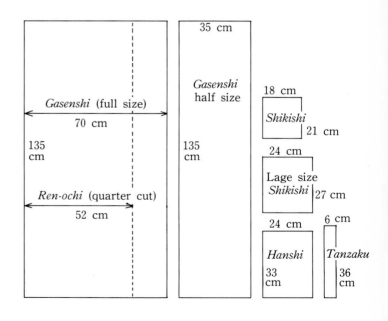

Size of papers for calligraphy use

What kind of Washi is used for Japanese painting?

J apanese painting is an art utilizing a technique which prevails throughout the world. Pigments taken from natural minerals, vegetables and animals are kneaded together with an animal glue called collagen. This coloring material is used for painting and this technique was the painting technique when mankind first began the act of painting. In that sense, it can be said that Japanese painting is not purely Japanese.

The murals of ancient Egypt, the icon paintings and also in India and China, paintings using glue are known.

However, due to the appearance of oil paintings and new color materials, this pan-global painting technique has, at present, been limited to few areas of the world and Japanese painting has become representative of paintings which value glue and natural pigments. The most important basic material supporting Japanese painting is *Washi*.

There are such basic materials as stonewalls, clay walls, wooden boards, silk and leather and Japanese painting are compatible with various materials but among them, *Washi* with its durability and beautiful texture, is the foundation of support for Japanese painting and it is possible to paint color thickly on it and utilize the texture of the paper.

Among *Washi* mostly used for present-day Japanese painting, the cloud texture hemp paper made by Heizaburo Iwano of Echizen (Fukui) is well known but in other periods, it seems that there was a

The artist painting on *Washi*

painter's preference or a sort of fashion for a particular *Washi* material.

Paper used for paintings during the *Muromachi* (1336-1573), *Momoyama* (1573-1603) and the *Yedo* (1603-1867) periods were mostly *Gampi Washi*. These were the ages when the beauty of the gold leaf and fineness of paper texture was preferred. There was an age when *Senshi* (cf. Glossary) using Chinese *Spindletree* bark as raw material was greatly utilized or many instances when the paintings prior to that age were painted on *Kozo* paper.

At present, the main technique of Japanese painting is to paint color material thickly so a thick hemp paper is preferred but Japanese painters in the past made efforts to search for *Washi* which is able to match the painting he desires to express.

The papermaker also had dialogue with the painter and such special *Washi* as *Gahoo-shi* or *Hooan-shi* (cf. Note) named after the painter were made and wielded a great influence on the individualistic painting expression of these painters.

In order to do away with criticism advocated a short time after the war that Japanese painting is a secondary art, the traditional technique was abandoned and expressionism valued. For that reason, it seems that attention was not paid to the basic *Washi* material. However, because of reflection on the damage to some painting due to disregard for technique, some artists appeared who started to pay attention again to the basic material and also papermakers who made paper to match his work of art. This kind of situation is an important matter when considering *Washi* and in the future, *Washi* suiting the artists' expression will be more in demand.

Japanese painting does not use paper in as great amount as is used for calligraphy, but high quality paper made from carefully selected material and long-lasting paper is required. For that reason, excessive processing or bleaching of fibers is disliked because it could cause spots and early deterioration of the paper. Also papers which can cope with usage of large amounts of *Dosa* sizing required to fix the color material is necessary.

Anyway, it is a fact that the many special characteristics which *Washi* possesses is an important factor sustaining Japanese painting and for the sake of Japanese painting which bears a part of the culture of Japan, communication between the artist and papermaker is desired.

Note
Gahoo
Gahoo Hashimoto(1835-1908)
Hooan
Hooan Kosugi(1861-1964)

Answer : **Isao Hayashi**

Tell us about Washi and printmaking.

In May, 1988, the Machida City International Printmaking Art Museum was planning a workshop to be conducted by a German artist, Horst Janssen. I said "was planning" because this invitation which was so expected, unfortunately could not be realized due to health problems cropping up just before departure from his country. However, his exclusive print technician, Freilinghaus came to Japan in his place and introduced a part of Janssen's work.

This technician, Freilinghaus was not just a printer but was an eccentric person and known as a expressionist of shocking erotic and masochistic human character. It was also thought he might be influencing in someway the images of Horst Janssen, the representative artist and leading printmaker of West Germany. Janssen was widely known for his watercolor works but after meeting Freilinghaus and especially after experiencing the printing effect on *Washi*, he seems to have become fascinated with copper plate etching as one possessed. It should be especially mentioned that the fact that Freilinghaus selected *Gampi* and *Mitsumata Washi* papers contributed greatly to the tremendous increase of work and a new development of expressionism since Janssen's fascination with copper plate etching.

As everyone knows, etching is a type of print medium expression which must leave the total completion of expression dependent on the printed effect. When we realize that in printing, not only

Trans position '84-ground-I 1984 62×102cm. Etching, Aquatint

technical skill but also selection of ink and paper has an important meaning, then it may be possible to fathom that Janssen's fascination to copper plate etching was in part due to his discovery of *Washi*.

In February, 1972, I was invited to the specially established Art Department of Kochi University and gave a concentrated lecture on copper plate etching. I knew Kochi was historically famous as a producing center of *Washi* and in between lectures, I visited those papermakers remaining in Takaoka and Ino-cho. At that time, the copper plate etching technique which had its roots in Europe was firmly established in Japan and it was a period when word of "etching boom" was even starting to be heard. However, regarding tools and materials for copper plate etching, paper was the only item that had to be imported from France. Carrying on the desire of the pioneer, Tetsuro Komai who worked very hard to establish genuine copper plate etching in Japan, it was my wish to foster this effort and I was hoping for a Japanese variation of copper plate etching using domestic materials and my visits to papermaking works was an idea with an eye to that objective.

Because of the thick and long inner bark fiber of *Kozo Washi*, it is not an appropriate paper for copper plate etching. Troubles arise, such as the tacky ink filling the concave areas of paper causing poor definition of print lines. However, paper called "Nacré" which is highly esteemed in France was thought to be made using Japanese techniques and also *Gampi* print, a technique often used by domestic artists as a method of printing by pasting a sheet of *Gampi* paper over western-style paper was resulting in a unique soft and tasteful effect so I thought there may be some room for innovation from these standpoints.

Fortunately, I was able to gain the acquaintence of the former Chief, Kaname Betchaku, of the Kochi Paper Industrial Laboratory and he agreed to assist in development of a new paper based on it's suitability for use in copper plate and lithograph printing.

Western-style paper used for printing was mainly made from rags in the past but in recent years, it is made from cotton pulp called linter. At that time, 2 kinds of printing paper made from cotton pulp were produced but including test papers made by the foresaid laboratory, these papers were not better than foreign papers which could also enhance the unique expressionism of the Japanese. For some time, exchange of test papers and results of test printing between the laboratory and myself continued. *Gampi* and *Mitsumata* papers were found to be highly adaptable to oleoginous ink and therefore suited the soft, delicate and aesthetic sense of the Japanese which has been fostered by a temperate climate. Finally, a newly created paper called N. B. paper was made by making a sheet by the *Tamezuki* method and overlaying it with a thin *Gampi* ply. It took 3

years to make it into a marketable product but with the timely opportunity of being involved with the movement for promotion of local industries by Kochi prefecture, Mr. & Mrs. Kanatoshi Ozaki of Ino-cho are making a wonderful paper with cotton pulp as a base. Moreover, it was found out that "Nacré" was a specially made *Mitsumata* paper.

Incidentally, Horst Janssen was an avid fan of *Ukiyoe* and was so enthusisastic that he once imagined himself as Hokusai and etched his own form fishing by the riverside. However, it is interesting to see that the most sensitive part of his artistic nature was printed on *Gampi* and *Mitsumata* paper. Admiration of the Orient in Europe is not a new development but it is unusual for anyone other than Janssen who has in a straight-forward manner injected his artistic style directly into *Washi*.

Intellect, emotion and volition comprise the mental factors of human beings and to me, it seems that "intellect" permeates western-style papers while "emotion" is interlocked into *Washi*. Compared to Europe where the object of paper was thought only to transmit, record and preserve "intellect", it seems to me that in Japan, "emotion" was described and also fostered by this vehicle.

European civilization has reached a saturation point and has come to a standstill. As a result, considering the situation where the Orient is being newly rediscovered at the end of this century, I am surely not the only one who

deems this development a great
point of interest.

Answer : **Tadayoshi Nakabayashi**

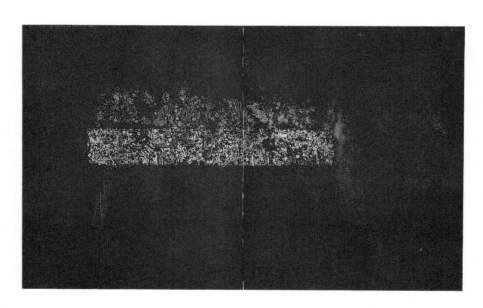

Trans position '87-ground-IV   1987 62×101cm.   Etching, Aquatint

What kind of arts and crafts of Washi are there? What sort of Washi is used?

Torn and pasted picture

Paper doll

As representative arts and crafts utilizing *Washi*, the following may be mentioned : cut and pasted pictures, torn and pasted pictures, paper flower making and paper dolls.

Cut and pasted and torn and pasted pictures are pictures drawn by use of paper which has been cut or torn. Mixing coloring material on a pallete to create various colors, like painting, is impossible. As the color of the dyed *Washi* is most important, beautifully dyed, non-fading high quality paper becomes necessary.

Paper cut with scissors is used for a pasted picture and handmade *Washi* is mainly used but at times, machine-made *Washi* is used in combination.

Paper torn by hand is pasted to make the picture and the "fluffiness" of the *Washi* when torn is valued, so handmade *Washi* made from *Kozo* and *Mitsumata* is used. There is absolutely no limit as to which *Washi* must be used but it is selected by the work of art, form of expression, etc..

As *Washi* is made by utilizing vegetable fibers as raw material, flowers made from *Washi* as compared to other imitation flowers will express a stronger likeness to real flowers and possess a unique elegance. Momoyo Kaifu who is the foremost maker of *Washi* flowers says, "On a certain later date, each person will gather up his (her) past memories and with peace in heart, create a flower. This is the best feeling and is my creed when making a *Washi* flower".

Washi dolls using *Washi* as the

basic material has as roots such dolls as *Kamibina* (doll festival paper dolls) and *Anesama Ningyo* (playing dolls). Doll art using *Washi* is unique to Japan but recently, appreciation of this art is high overseas.

Those who wish to start doll-making should use *Chiyogami* (paper with colored, woodblock printed patterns) or *Yuzen Kata-zome* (paper stencil-dyed with decorative *Yuzen* textile patterns). When one desires to give the doll a gentle expression or movement, *Chirimen Momigami* (creped crumpled paper) or *Konnyaku*(devil's tongue) treated decorated paper is the best. From there on, it is up to the artist's imagination as to what he or she wants use. The variety is countless such as *Itajime* (fold and dye paper), *Bijitsu Sukimoyoogami* (paper made with artistic decorations on it) or *Kamiko* (paper clothing) to clothe the doll.

This can be said about each art and craft but by becoming acquainted with as many kinds of *Washi* as possible, the breadth of expression of the item to be made shall become broader. Also, by handling many different kinds of paper, you will become more and more fascinated by *Washi*.

Answer : **Tomoko Omura**

Paper flowers

Tell us about Origami (Paper-folding).

Origami was introduced to Japan around the 6th century from China. At that time, besides writing, paper was used to wrap offerings to the deities (salt, etc.). At a traditional wedding in Japan, the *sake*-bottle is decorated with male and female paper butterflies. It can be considered that paper was originally a material to be used in sacred rites.

Recently, among younger people, a wrapping boom has arisen and methods of gift wrapping have also been devised. A variga-ted development such as from "folding, wrapping, tieing" to "folding up, stacking, etc" has taken place.

The history of Japanese *origami* first started during the end of the *Heian* period (794-1192) when Kiyosuke of the Fujiwara family folded paper into the shape of a frog. During the *Kamakura* period (1192-1333) when nobles bestowed swords, etc. , there was a custom of attaching an *origami* on the list of contents. Even today, the words "*origami* attached" remains which signifies historical or pedigree guarantee. Later, during the *Muromachi* period (1338-1573) paper-folding became one of the skills to be learned for good manners (etiquette) and developed into the *Ogasawara* school, *Ise* school and *Saga* school.

On the other hand, when the material called paper became easy to obtain during the *Yedo* period (1603-1867), *origami* spread through the populance as a plaything of the masses. In the story "A Generation of an Amorous Fellow" written by Saikaku Ihara (1642-1693), a scene of paper-folding is depicted. Even at present, when a prayer is offered "a thousand cranes" are folded. This endearing custom has been carried on for ages.

A few years ago, an American television station took up the themes of "*Origami*", "*Sake* (Japanese wine)" and "*Matsuri* (Festivals)" as representative of Japanese culture and the writer supplied information on *origami*. Reviewing the videotape sent me, the opening scene of "*Origami*" showed an employee at the sales booth of a department store skillfully rolling and wrapping up a round can of biscuits. It seems that everyday wrapping is seen by foreigners as a part of the *origami* genre.

A certain Frenchman who wrote in a handbook of *origami* gave as examples, ceremonial envelopes, written oracles, fans, wrapping of powdered medicine, kimonos and obis (sashes). In these Japanese acts of folding, folding up, tieing, stacking, etc., there is multi-colored beauty and sureness of hand work.

I have always felt that as a Japanese it is a pity to leave traditional aesthetic sense asleep which was born naively and naturally from the long history in which we are living. Not only as a hobby, the action taken in folding a sheet of paper and making it into a three dimension figure has educational effect which fosters concentration, creativity and the feeling of discipline. It is recognized that the movement of the fingertips has such medical effects as stimulation of the brain, helping its development and prevention of senility. Thus, *origami* is currently encouraged in the educational field and at rehabilitation centers and has proved to be effective. Also in geometry and in the aeronautical engineering field of computer graphics, I hear that old and new *origami* is an object of research.

Before, Japanese children learned *origami* at home or at school and enjoyed themselves making simple and complex *origami*. With the times, play has changed and *origami* has been discarded as educational material and not many children make *origami* any more. On the other hand, ironically, attention has been paid by schools in Europe, U.S.A., Mexico, New Zealand, etc. where lessons and lectures have been held and *origami* artists and enthusiasts are increasing throughout the world.

Japan has a long history of a unique paper called *Washi* which is thin and strong. This fact is the origin of the word *"origami"* which is now in common use throughout the world. Paper made from vegetation breathes and lives. I believe that to become intimate with *origami* is the same as directly touching and conversing with the origin of our great nature.

Origami transcends time, disregards location, can be made by both adults and children and in spite of a language barrier, with only one piece of paper, one can share joy with people of the world by creating a form with one's fingertips. *Origami* may be made with any kind of paper lying around you but I wish that you would see with your own eyes, feel with your own hands and challenge the traditional industrial art product, *Washi*—the softness and strength of it's delicate texture, it's abundant variety and beautiful differing colors. *Washi* should take you to an endless world. *Origami* which has been inherited by us, is, in my perception, the most peaceful of pastimes.

Answer : **Kazuo Kobayashi**

Tell us about wrapping and Washi.

"Wrapping" is one of the main functions of paper. Recently, it is reported that what is said to be the oldest paper in the world unearthed in China was wrapped around a bronze mirror. From this illustration, it is also said that perhaps, the object of papermaking was to wrap items. Anyway, it is certain that paper was not just a vehicle for writing. The paper of that ancient age was made by recycling rags and was probably cheaper than cloth and it was only natural that the public noticed that it was an excellent wrapping material. In the relation between man and goods, it is only natural, in our daily life, to use one thing in many ways. The act of "wrapping" is to collect the contents together, protect it, transport it and to make it easier to deliver. The representative wrapping device of Japan was probably the "*Furoshiki*" (a wrapping cloth). The benefit of using the *furoshiki* which is able to contain different kinds of articles and wrap them in one piece of cloth should be highly evaluated as Japanese resourcefulness. Though the object of wrapping may be the same, in case of *Washi*, because of its physical character, it takes a different shape than the freeness of the *furoshiki*. Generally, compared to cloth, paper is thin, light and has tensile strength. It's strength cannot rival cloth but the price is cheap. In the days when paper was a valuable item, waste paper, recycled paper, or paper made by accumulating waste raw material and cheap papers which could not be used for other purposes were probably used.

In case of "wrapping", the paper is creased alongside the contents and then wrapped. For that reason, wrapping paper is reborn in a form newly restructured by straight lines. To enjoy such change and in accordance with the difference of the contents, different kinds of wrapping methods are devised by each generation. When using *Washi*, the wrapped form itself is beautiful. Also, the whiteness inherent to the paper is a symbol of purity and chastity and was a vital basic material for those who mastered ceremonies. Such skills as cutting and folding, etc. was applied to *Washi* and was often used as pendant paper strips in shrines, in congratulatory events and festive rites. Also, such traditional customs as the use of money envelopes and betrothal gift goods which are tied in with etiquette and linked to our daily living, is still practiced today.

Those papers called *"tsutsumigami"* or *"hosooshi"* (both meaning wrapping paper in Japanese) came to be called "Wrapping paper" in the last 20 years. After World War 2, in all areas of food, clothing and shelter, the westernized influence became more evident and mass consumption became fixed as a social arrangement. *"Zoto-hin"* (presents), *"Chugen"* (mid-year gift) and *"Seibo"* (year-end gift) all came to be called "gifts" and *"hosooshi"* became "wrapping paper". Originally, paper was an item attached to the merchandise and had no value but suddenly, attention became focused on wrapping material itself. A growing number of specialty stores to handle gift merchandise only, imported and displayed a variety of beautiful wrapping paper. Initially, these stores mainly handled imports but with increased competition and overheating of this boom, higher grade goods were in demand and efforts were made in developing individualistic designs. However, with mass produced machine-made paper, discrimination of paper quality was naturally limited. Therefore, the main object of designing became paper processing by printing, chemical treatment or embossing, etc. i.e. all kinds of paper processing techniques were freely employed to create an appealing product.

It is only natural that *Washi* became tied into this booming market. Viewing the quality of the paper itself, it is evident that *Washi* is superior quality-wise. Though printing may not be suitable, dyeing can be done without restraint and its strength and light weight make it suitable for wrapping. Moreover, the strong point of *Washi* is its emotional appeal and the richness directly felt when handled amplifies the sentiment of the sender.

It is hardly possible that the wrapping industry should neglect this situation. Together with know-how on various ways of wrapping, *Washi* became a part of the wrapping market. Since then, 10 years have elapsed and even at present, a small amount is marketed as the highest grade wrapping paper available. Though it may not be called a boom, it is expected even hereafter that it will continue to keep a share of the market supported by faithful enthusiasts. However, when looking at *Washi* wrapping as merchandise, the display arrangement is poor. In case of western-style papers, wrapping paper wrapped on paper cores or wrapped in cellophane have already a permanent market. To sell wrapping papers wrapped up does not seem to be right but in order to channel this merchandise in the current market system, it is an unavoidable standardization.

If *Washi* is handled in the same method, such direct appealing factors as the sense of touch and the warmth inherent to *Washi* itself would be difficult to be conveyed. However, if it is uncovered, it will be a sad and unfortunate sight if left in a sales space dirtied by the surrounding atmosphere. The concern of those who love *Washi* and those managers of shops who desire to continue to supply *Washi* can be easily imagined. On top of that, the high production cost cannot be compared. Faced with such difficult problems, there are many shops which have given up handling of *Washi*. The present time is very important as to whether *Washi* is able to gain a footing in the world's common wrapping market or not. The producer should not only rely upon cultural background of *Washi* but it is necessary to question oneself whether *Washi* is effective or not as a means of more richer communication.

Currently, this is an age where people are examining paper and questioning its quality. From the global environment conservation standpoint, recycled paper and *Washi* are being highlighted. Paper is slowly but surely moving towards the situation where the function of paper is requested to be a vehicle of emotion as apart from being a vehicle of information.

I believe that in this situation, as a basic material to suit the aspiration of the consumer, *Washi* wrapping will be accepted by the people.

Answer : **Kyoko Ibe**

What kind of Washi is used in mounting?

The term "mounting" means mounting of hangings, scrolls, folding screens, framed paintings, sliding doors and also includes repair and mending of antiques.

Either in the East or West, after drawings, paintings, or calligraphy leave the artists' hand, they are finished by the mounting craftsman into hangings and folding screens. What supports these artistic forms is paper on the back side and what they have in common is that it is all done by *Washi*. (especially *Kozo* paper).

For instance, taking a hanging scroll as an illustration, there are three stages of work, back surface mounting, additional back mounting and total back mounting using such *Kozo* papers as *Minogami*, *Misugami* and *Udagami* (cf. Glossary) separately.

Mounted works of art which have deteriorated over the years, need to be repaired by mounting craftsmen. Their main work is to renew the mounting paper. By this work, the work of art is passed on to the present and it is necessary to say that the quality of the supporting *Washi* paper is very important.

The manufacturing process of paper due to technical advancement uses strong chemicals, so the inherent qualities of *Washi* such as strength and aesthetic appearance disappear and too often the paper is too white, the fiber weakens or the paper becomes acidic. It is evident that this kind of paper is not good for old works of art.

Also, drawings, paintings and calligraphy which have been damaged by insects must be repaired using the same high quality of paper. Better *Washi* making techniques of not only *Kozo* paper but also *Gampi* and *Mitsumata* are needed to make paper which can be used to restore and repair those works of art.

Such mountings and those craftsmen engaged in such work have a close relation inseparably bound with *Washi*.

Answer : **Iwataro Oka**

How is Washi used in architecture such as in homes or buildings?

It is said Japanese houses are made of wood and paper. That was the traditional way of life. Paper has been used in many ways: on the floor, a *Yutan* (paper carpet), for open room spaces, sliding panel paper and sliding door papers, for the lower part of sand walls, *Minatogami* (cf. Glossary), for walls and ceilings, for room partitions, screens and folding screens and for lighting.

To keep out draught in winter, a large paper enclosure was hung up in the room. A hanging paper scroll is often hung in the *Tokonoma* (alcove). Even for bedding, *Kamifusuma* (paper bed cover quilt) and for *Kamiko* (paper clothing) or *Shifu* (paper cloth), *Washi* was used.

For interior design, there is no country outside of Japan which has skillfully developed such a varigated culture using paper. It was the papermakers who made strong, clean *Washi*, the craftsmen who added beautiful designs and manufactured various articles of daily necessity and the sure aesthetic sense of those who introduced these items into their daily lives who made this possible.

However, today, the paper interior materials used in architecture are mainly for sliding panels and sliding doors. Vinyl plastic has replaced wall paper. The house owner, designer and contractor have since the war, placed too much importance on economics, function and easy construction so that they have ignored paper which is a more delicate construction material.

However, once we step into a

traditional private house or ceremonial tea house, why do we feel enveloped in a nostalgic peacefulness? Differing from such nonorganic material as concrete, steel and glass or such non-organic and hard material as synthetic resin, paper and wood once were living. Therefore, they respond to our inner psychology and speak to us with strong and silent words. The whisper of paper is deep and when our feelings are insensitive, that voice cannot be heard.

40 years have passed since the end of war and the livelihood of the Japanese has gradually returned to a settled life and it seems that more people are having another look at the good quality of *Washi*.

In ending, listed here are some points to consider when using *Washi* for interior decoration.

1. There are no restrictions on sliding panels and sliding doors but when using *Washi* on walls or ceiling, please check construction limitations. Even if resticted, there are some *Washi* products which will qualify.

2. Between handmade and machine-made *Washi*, there are differences in taste, quality, specifications and price. Please select according to the budget.

3. Regarding 10-30 years long-run value, handmade *Washi* for sliding panels or sliding doors is economical.

4. If mounting work is not appropriate, the paper will deteriorate or fade with time. It is important not to cut down on backmounting costs.

5. Abundant designs on *Washi* are available and special order designs even for 1 sheet can be made. Creative designing is possible.

6. It is possible to include *Washi* material to modern interior decoration. Consult a *Washi* store about your wishes.

7. Regarding special characteristics or actual work, please consult experienced paperhangers, mounters or approved wall paper stores.

Answer : **Mitsuhiro Ban**

It is said printing on Washi is difficult. Why?

In present day Japan, printing technique for western-style papers maintains the highest level in the world. With this technique, multi-color printing on *Washi* is highly possible and in the future, there is a great outlook opening up in development of the printing sphere. However, for that objective, it is necessary to overcome some technically unsolved problems.

Up to the beginning of the *Meiji* period (1867-1926), all printed matter in Japan was on *Washi*. From the 1870's on, western-style paper production increased and printing paper switched to western-style paper and the printing method changed from surface printing to lithograph printing and at present, color printing is very popular. During this time, even in the monochrome genre, *Washi* printing was restricted to a specialty field and multi-colored printing was regarded as hopeless. But is color printing on *Washi* hopeless?

Among readers of this book, I believe there are some who have seen *Washi* calendars at year end. These calendars are color printed on *Washi* made by expert papermakers of producing areas, carrying sketches of the ancient capital by the famous Japanese painting artist Isao Hayashi and printed by experienced printing technicians.

In this age of western-style papers which has a history of a 100 years, printing machines, printing ink and platemaking technology have all been made to adapt to western-style papers. However, looking back, color printing on western-style papers was not an entire success from the beginning. Even color prints about 20 years ago had color overruns and poor reproduction of photographs. Moreover, the colors of printing ink were not natural and were poor goods compared to present color printings. The people engaged in printing technology modified this situation together and reached the present-day high standard.

If papermakers and printing experts would study together and make efforts, color printing of *Washi* could be carried out much easier but the truth is that such efforts were not exerted and all concerned gave it up as hopeless.

World famous *Washi* has characteristics not available in western-style papers. If this *Washi* was printed with beautiful subjects equal to western-style papers, this would not only help in spreading reproduction and preservation of cultural assets, special printings and drawings but also *Washi* could be kept alive in everyday life. In this way, it would help greatly in the inheritance, dissemination and development of Japanese culture. This would also tie in with expansion of the printing area and also increase demand for *Washi*.

Especially, in the future, regarding problems to increase the printing area to *Washi* printing, the following matters can be considered.

1. How to maintain the smoothness of *Washi* without losing its special characteristics of good texture and beauty.

2. Means to find methods to prevent show-through of ink.

3. Prevention of peeling or fluffing of paper. Modification of strong adhesiveness of printing ink to fit *Washi*.

4. Prevention of stretch or shrinking of paper. The printing machine prints while pulling the paper strongly. In case of multi-color printing, it will pull the paper as many times as the color differs so the printing structure must be improved. Again, in case of offset printing, the use of water will become the cause of stretch and shrink, so that must be altered.

5. Modification of *Washi* so paper lint does not appear. Compared to western-style papers, there is much lint and as the printing plate becomes soiled, printing cannot be clearly done so *Washi* papermakers must also make efforts to modify their product.

These problems were, in the past, inherent in western-style paper printing but have been improved and modified. Of course, this problem can be overcome by the combined efforts of *Washi* papermakers, those engaged in printing machinery and material manufacturing. I look forward to the day that is accomplished and to the time when multi-colored printed *Washi* is spread throughout the world.

Answer : **Shohei Asano**

Hand-fed offset printer

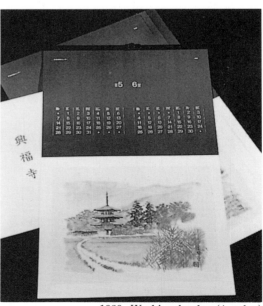

1989 *Washi* calender (4 color)

WASHI
PRODUCTION AREAS
AND
CHARACTERISTICS

Festival parasol

Washi Producing Areas and Characteristics

TOHOKU-KANTO AREA

● *Iwate Prefecture*
Higashiyama Washi

A refugee of the overthrown Fujiwara clan seated at Hiraizumi (Hiraizumi-cho, Nishi Iwai-gun, Iwate) first engaged in papermaking as a side line to farming and produced this *Washi* for use in daily life. It has a tradition of about 800 years. In 1942, 285 persons were engaged in papermaking but in 1988, only 4 papermakers have continued *Washi* production.

The raw material is the bark of cultivated *Kozo* and this paper has a natural *Kozo* color and a taste of fineness and elegance while being strong, so it is favored and used for *Shojigami* (cf. Glossary) and various other folkcraft items.

● *Miyagi Prefecture*
Shiroishi Washi

A special local species of paper mulberry (*Kajinoki*) is cultivated and is used to make a pure paper mulberry fiber *Washi*. This paper is soft and strong so it is appropriate for *Shifu* (woven paper cloth), *Kamiko* (paper clothing), calligraphy and drawing paper, *Katazome* (stencil dyeing paper), permanent preservation recording paper, wallpaper etc.. The paper produced today is the characteristic *Michinokugami* (cf. Glossary) which has been made since the *Heian* period (794-1192).

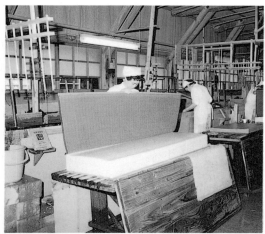

Washi mill (Ohzu Washi)

● *Fukushima Prefecture*
Toonoshi

Raw material is 100% *Kozo* and is a winter made unbleached paper. This is a pure *Washi* made by the traditional method, meaning that *Kozo* is prepared into white bark, boiled with soda ash, hand beaten, handmade and dried naturally. The papermaking history of Katoono dates back to the *Eiroku* years (1558-1569) and due to encourgement of the Tanakura clan, *Toonoshi* was highly valued as *Yedo* samurai recording paper. In addition, the accounting ledger paper called *Nobegami* was also famous.

The paper is strong and has an elegant luster so is widely used for calligraphy paper, drawing paper (especially India ink painting), various paper arts (dolls, dyed paper, paper flowers, torn paper picture, pasted paper picture, *Shifu*, Japanese-style notebook, etc.) paper for taking impressions, *Katagami* (stencil dyeing paper), *Fudagami* (cf. Glossary), blockprint paper, vegetable wax dyeing paper, permanent preservation recording paper, general use paper and *Shojigami*.

● *Tochigi Prefecture*
Karasuyama Washi

This paper has been traditionally made in Karasuyamashi located in eastern Tochigi. It has been handed down from about 1200 years ago. The reason papermaking started here is perhaps due to the natural gift of clear water from Naka river which flows from the Nasu mountain range.

This *Washi* is represented by *Hodomurashi* (cf. Glossary) but many other kinds of paper are made. It is known for its paper strength and elegance and the main characteristic is that it uses *Kozo* cultivated in the Nasu area and is famous for its fold resistance.

It is also well known for its making of *Kaishi* (cf. Glossary) for ceremonial use at the Imperial Household.

● *Ibaragi Prefecture*
Nishinouchi Washi

It is said that the history of *Washi* in Ibaragi is as old as 1500 years. *Washi* made by utilizing the clear water of Kuji river which originates from Mt. Yamizo rising above the boundries of Ibaragi, Fukushima and Tochigi. This paper was named *Nishinouchi* (cf. Glossary) by the venerable Lord Mitsukuni, second Lord of the Mito clan during the *Tokugawa* period (1603-1867). This paper is famous even today as it was used for the "*Dai Nippon-Shi* (History of Greater Japan, 397 volumes, started 1657) which was a selection of history compiled by Lord Mitsukuni. The paper is made even today in the locality of Nishinouchi, Yamagata-cho, Naka-gun, Ibaragi.

Nishinouchishi folded in half came to be known as *Hanshi* (half-sized paper) and three sheets joined together came to be called *Hangiri* (half cuts). At present, besides being made for calligraphy paper, Japanese painting paper, India ink drawing paper and woodblock paper, it is made for permanent preservation paper.

● *Yamanashi Prefecture*
Nishijima Washi

This paper which has a history of about 450 years was favored by Lord Shingen Takeda as calligraphy paper. Later, after viscisitudes of time, it has continued up to the present, centering on production of calligraphy paper such as *Gasenshi* (cf. Glossary) and *Hanshi* (cf. Glossary).

The main raw material is waste paper (mainly *Mitsumata*) but straw, bamboo, etc. are mixed in. The ink color, blur, finish of the brush and brush application all are delicately expressed on this paper and it is praised by calligraphy experts as an excellent calligraphy paper.

● *Shizuoka Prefecture*
Suruga Hanshi, Shuzenjishi

Washi known as *Suruga Hanshi* or *Shuzenjishi* produced in the western part of Shizuoka. has a long history and tradition originating from the *Nara* period (710-794). In recent times, during the height of prosperity, with development of the tea industry, there were about 70 papermaking villages.

The main raw materials are *Kozo*, *Mitsumata* and *Gampi* and especially, after cultivation of *Mitsumata* became possible, production of *Suruga Hanshi* flourished. At present, a great amount is produced and paper made from "matured *Mitsumata* waste" is favored by calligraphy experts.

Suruga Yunogami

This paper is produced in an area centered on Yuno, Shibakawa-cho located at the eastern foot of Mt. Fuji and is made by utilizing the large natural spring water from the famous Shiraito Falls.

The main raw material of this paper is bark of *Kozo*, *Mitsumata* and *Gampi* and the paper is handmade and dried naturally on *Tochi* (horse chestnut, Aesculus chinensis) boards. For that reason, it has a unique luster and feeling and a tranquil character. If the preservation method is suitable, it is widely favored as a permanent preservation paper.

● *Saitama Prefecture*
Ogawa Washi (Hosokawashi cf. Glossary)

It seems that the origin of this paper starts back in the 8th century. This is due to the reason that at that time, Buddhist temples were constructed in various areas and a great amount of sutra copy paper was necessary.

In the 17th century, after the Tokugawa Shogunate government was established, the daily use of paper of the populance increased and the demand for *Washi* for such uses as publishing books, account books for trade dealings, etc. grew annually. As a supply source, this area (at present, the area around Ogawa-cho, Hiki-gun, Saitama) developed into a large papermaking center.

The traditional technique of the other name of *Ogawa Washi* i.e. "*Hosokawashi*" has been designated as an Important Intangible Cultural Asset and papermaking still continues up to the present.

Wazo Odaka

CHUBU AREA

● *Niigata Prefecture*
Echigo Washi

In the records of *Shoso-In* of the *Nara* period (710-794), it mentions that paper was made in Echigo (Niigata) and Sado (island off Niigata) which proves that *Echigo Washi* has a long history. In 1988, the *Washi* producing areas in Niigata totalled eight : 2 papermakers in Kawakami-mura, Higashi Kambara-gun (Koide *Washi*, Prefectural Intangible Cultural Asset), 1 in Kamo-shi, 1 in Takayanagi-cho, Kariwa-gun, 2 in Oguni-cho, Kariwa-gun and 2 in Yunotani-mura, Kita Uonuma-gun.

In areas with much snowfall, *Kozo* is cultivated in summer and made into to paper as side work in winter when snow falls and piles up. Here, papermaking follows a traditional method of snow bleaching of *Kozo* fibers and burying the newly made wet sheets in snow, recovering them in March when clear bright days increase and then board drying them.

The paper made is either bleached or unbleached *Kozo* paper and is used widely as *Shojigami*, printing paper, woodblock paper, kite paper, lantern paper and dyed paper.

Some paper is used for vegetable dye paper as the paper quality is high. It is both strong and sincere with a distinctive classic *Washi* feeling.

In March, 1988, all Niigata papermakers formed the "Echigo Handmade Washi Society" and mutual dialogue between papermakers became closer and in each producing center, the succeeding generation has been fostered and are continuing to uphold the tradition.

● *Toyama Prefecture*
Etchu Washi

In *Shoso-In* records (written about 750) the name of "*Etchu Washi*" can be seen together with *Echizen* (Niigata) and *Mino*

(Gifu) *Washi* so Toyama is also an area where the art of papermaking started early in Japan.

The paper flourished after the feudal clan system was established and Uchi Yao-cho was the only papermaking area in the Toyama clan which produced medicine wrapping paper for the Etchu patent medicine as well as other papers. Tairamura Gokakami also realized an increasing market and need of such papers *Shojigami*, etc. for consumption in the neighboring large Kaga clan.

Present production centers are 3 paper mills located at Yatsuo-machi, Nei-gun (55 employees), 4 paper mills in Taira-mura, Higashi Tonami-gun (30 employees), 1 mill in Hirugaya, Asahi-cho, Shimo Shinkawa-gun (3 employees). Both Yatsuo-machi and Hiranuma mills are specialized mills and the production scale is preeminent in Japan.

The paper is 100% *Kozo* and is a reliable paper made in line with traditional methods. At Yatsuo-machi, dyed paper, *Momigami* (cf. Glossary) and paper for various uses are made and the quality and beautiful coloring of the dyed paper have an established reputation. Tairamura Gokakami produces *Shojigami*, recording paper, lantern paper, calligraphy and drawing papers and at Hirugaya Asahi-cho, *Shojigami* and India ink drawing paper is produced. All these papers are called "*Etchu Washi*" and are designated as Japanese Traditional Industrial Art Items.

Making of design papers by stencil dyeing and making of pouches and other processed goods utilizing the strength of the paper is flourishing. On top of that, papermakers are actively contemplating development of new uses such as in the interior decoration and architechture field.

● *Ishikawa Prefecture*
Kaga Washi

During the *Yedo* period (1603-1867) when this area was governed by the Kaga clan, paper used for formal ceremonies was called *Goryoshi*. Paper produced for *Goryoshi*, clan bank notes, wrapping paper to seal silver foil, etc. were, in total, called *Kaga Washi*.

From old times, the traditional art of gold and silver foil beating flourished in Ishikawa and connected with this, *Hakuuchi-shi* (paper for beating foil) was made in large amounts.

The present production centers in Ishikawa are Kanazawa-shi, Futamata-cho (3 papermakers), Tajima-cho (2), Wajima-shi (1), Kawakita-cho, Nomi-gun (1), Torigoe-mura, Ishikawa-gun (1).

At Futamata-cho, Obi (Japanese sashes made by *Kamiko* technique), Kaga color *Hosho, Sukigata moyooshi* (cf. Glossary) and *Gampi* paper containing clay used for finishing of foil beating are made. In this area, cultivation of *Kozo* and an establishment for experiencing papermaking by laymen is projected.

At Wajima, *Gasenshi* mixed with bamboo and cryptomeria bark fibers are made, at Kitagawa-cho, *Gampi* papers containing clay and at Torigoe-mura, 100% *Kozo* paper for upper and lower cover paper for foil beating is made.

Shoji Yamaguchi

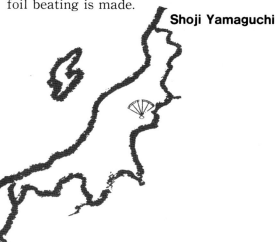

● *Kyoto*
Kurodani Washi

Papermaking in Kurodani is said to have been started in old times by fugitive warriors of the *Heike* clan and handed on to their descendents. It has a tradition of about 800 years and is still continued today.

The characteristics of this *Washi* is, as common in all areas, utilization of good quality *Kozo* growing in the mountains of Tamba and Tango and clear water springs which are suitable for papermaking. From these natural blessings, a strong *Washi* was created. At present, there are only 3 or 4 *Kozo* papermakers but they continue the old papermaking method and produce paper while handing down the traditional technique to posterity.

This paper was made in the old days in an outlying area but today, as transportation has become easier, it has come to the attention of those concerned. It has been designated as a Kyoto Intangible Cultural Asset and is processed into many paper products which are then supplied to the market.

Tango Washi

This paper is made by carefully bleaching in the mountain stream of Isuzu river, the high quality *Kozo* cultivated in the vicinity of Mt. Oye (famous for the legend of repulsing of the ogre). The characteristic of this paper is that it is a folkcraft paper colored with vegetable dyes. It has a tradition of 120 years and at one time, over 200 papermakers were engaged in making *Washi* but at present, only 2 papermakers are still keeping up this tradition.

In 1975, it was designated Oye-cho Intangible CulturalAsset and at present, papermakers are producing calligraphy paper, folkcraft paper, etc. in the Futamata area, Oye-machi, Kasa-gun, Kyoto.

● *Shiga Prefecture*
Ohmi Naruko Washi

In the *Engi-Shiki* (cf. Question 8) it is recorded that Ohmi (Shiga) was paying government taxes with paper and paper hemp (raw material). From old times, raw material was abundant and *Washi* production was flourishing.

During the *Bunsei* years (1821-1831) the technique for making *Naruko Washi* was introduced from Echizen (Fukui) and paper was made by using *Gampi* which grew wild in the mountains. Especially, during the *Meiji* and *Taisho* periods (1867-1926) a great amount of paper for gold and silver thread (cf. Glossary) used for the famous Kyoto Nishijin textiles was made.

Gampi paper from this area is strong and densely made. It is characterized by delicacy, elegance and soft texture. From the special qualities of *Gampi*, it is drawing attention as a permanent preservation paper and it is a well-known fact that a special run of *Naruko Washi* was supplied for the picture scroll entombed in the time capsule of the World Exposition to be preserved for 5000 years.

At present, this area is not only making *Gampi* papers but are also engaged in making various kinds of paper such as *Kozo* papers and light-colored dyed papers, etc..

● *Fukui Prefecture*
Echizen Washi

The name of this *Washi* can be seen in the annals of *Shoso-In* of the old *Nara* period (710-794). In the samurai society of the middle ages, demand for *Hoshoshi* increased and among them, *Echizen Hosho* and *Torinoko* (cf. Glossary) papers gained a high reputation as quality papers and the Echizen area came to be known as a representative *Washi* producing center.

Originally, *Echizen Washi* developed in the area located in the center of Fukui i. e. Goka area of Imadate-cho (Furoo, Ohtaki, Iwamoto, Shinzaike and Sadatomo) and even at present, about 100 household industries are engaged in handmade, machine-made papermaking and paper processing. The products are *Fusumagami* (sliding panel paper), *Komagami* (cf. Glossary), *Hoshoshi, Danshi* (cf. Glossary), *Shokenyoshi* (security paper), *Gasenshi*, etc.. The abundance and variety is unrivaled.

The pulp stock for this paper is stubbornly and strictly selected and the paper made retains a subtle nature. For sheet drying, the female *Ginkgo* tree boards are persistently used and it is a proud paper with fine and elegant texture.

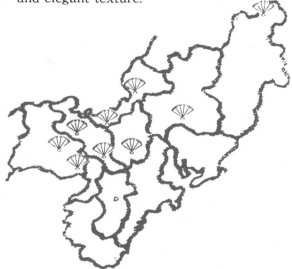

Wakasa Washi

During the reign of Tadakatsu Sakai, Lord of the Wakasa clan, cultivation of *Kozo* and *Mitsumata* was encouraged and papermaking in Nakanada made rapid progress. The products are ledger paper and base paper for paper umbrellas.

After the war, papermakers were members of the Fukui. Industrial Cooperative A'ssn| but 2 years later, they decided to become independent and as a technical reform they shifted from white papers to dyed papers such as *Yuzen* (*Yuzen* stencil dyeing), *Shibori* (tie dyeing), *Itajime* (fold and dye), *Bokashigami* (color gradation) for folkcraft use. Through these measures,

the name of *Wakasa Washi* came to be known and at present, an association has been formed with 7 papermakers and 2 dyers as active members. The "Wakasa Washi no Ie" (Wakasa Washi House) located at Toojiki, Obama-shi is engaged in direct sales.

● *Hyogo Prefecture*
Sugihara-gami

This paper is a *Kozo* paper produced at the early papermaking area, Sugihara-dani (present Kami-cho) located in Harima (Hyogo) and sutra copy paper and thin papers have been made here since the *Nara* period (710-794). During the *Muromachi* period (1336-1573), it was a written rule that "A samurai should not write on any other paper but *Sugihara*", so this paper was used widely as a samurai's writing paper and for government correspondence.

Kozo grows abundantly in this area and good water flows from the deep valleys. Utilizing these natural benefits and through tireless ingenuity and effort, *Sugihara* paper has| been| favored for| over |1000 years as a distinguished paper.

However, like other producing areas, due to a decrease in raw materials and change of occupation, production stopped at the end of the *Taisho* period (1926) but the people of Kami-cho revived this tradition and at present, by efforts of Masayasu Inoue, *Sugihara* paper is being produced again.

Nashioshi

The beginning of this paper goes back to the age of civil wars (about 400 years ago) when Saint Renjo visited this area and Yaumon Higashiyama (1596-1623) learned the papermaking method of *Echizen Washi* and started papermaking here. He especially conceived the idea of mixing clay and even today, *Nashio* paper is famous for it's *Kin-Hakuuchishi* (gold foil beating paper, cf. Glossary).

The characteristic of *Nashioshi* is the clay mixture production which cannot be made elsewhere. The method is to crush concentrated lime which is stirred in water and then mixing the suspended particles (bentonite) into the paper pulp. The paper has resistance against both moisture and dryness, preservation life is long, repels insects and due to the clay it is heat resistant. It has a soft luster and elegant simplicity.

As to the variety of paper, there is the *Nashio Maniaishi* (cf. Glossary), *Nashio Uchikumo* (cf. Glossary), *Hakushita* (cf. Glossary), *Kin-gin Hakuuchishi* and other folkcraft papers which are produced at Nashio, Shiose-machi, Nishinomiya-shi, Hyogo.

● *Nara Prefecture*
Yoshino-gami

In ancient Nara, the south mountainous area near Yoshino was the center of papermaking and the paper was called *Nara Gashi* (elegant Nara paper) and was used in abundance. In 1540, the name of the paper changed from the area name of Nara to the producing area of Yoshino and up to today, this Yoshino name is generally used.

The characteristic of this paper is that it is a thin *Kozo* paper and so thin that it is called "Yoshino softies". Especially, utilizing this characteristic, it is guaranteed to be the best paper adapted to filter lacquer.

White clay obtained from the mountains of Yoshino is mixed with the paper pulp and formed to create calligraphy paper which is highly esteemed as the best.

Also, at present, *Yamato Uda* paper (cf. Glossary) is produced and is widely used as a backing paper for mounting and for the same mounting use, a middle backing paper called *Misu* paper (cf. Glossary) is made. The characteristic of this paper is that after sheet-forming the wet sheet is immediately taken off the screen and dried on drying boards so both texture and strength have a subtlety which is said to be the masterpiece of *Kozo* papers. At present, 16 papermakers are working hard to produce this paper.

● *Nagano Prefecture*
Uchiyama Washi

This paper is also called *Uchiyama Shoin* (cf. Glossary) and is known as a pure white *Shojigami* preferred by city dwellers. Iiyama-shi, Nozawa-mura and Sakai-mura, Shimo Takai-gun are areas with the highest snowfall in Japan, and the special characteristic of this paper is that the *Kozo* bark is bleached white by the "*Yuki Zarashi*" (snow bleaching) method. When snow time comes, summer-grown *Kozo* is used as raw material and everybody begins papermaking. The characteristic of this 100% *Kozo Washi* is that it has not only strength but permits ventilation and passing of light.

● *Gifu Prefecture*
Mino Washi

Mino (Gifu), Chikuzen (Fukuoka) and Buzen (between Fukuoka and Oita) papers were used for family registration in the 2nd year of *Taiho* (710) and among those family register papers, the fibers of the *Mino* produced *Washi* were uniformly entwined and there was no unevenness which indicates it was the best among these papers. Also, at the end of this year, the Kiso mountain road (from West Nagano to Magome pass, 120 kilometers) was opened which was also an industrial route so the territory of Mino has maintained an important position from the past to the present as an advanced papermaking area.

The characteristic of *Mino Washi* is that it has a uniform surface. This is achieved by skillful repetition of vertical and horizontal movement of the screen. It has a high quality reputation superior to other local papers.

This paper is designated as an Intangible Important Cultural Asset. At present about 40 papermakers are producing art paper, folkcraft paper, *Ise Katagami* (cf. Glossary), and mounting paper.

Takashi Mame

CHUGOKU AREA

In the 3 prefectures of Hiroshima, Okayama and Yamaguchi, there are a few *Washi* producing areas left. Yokono in Tsuyama-shi, Okayama is a producing area of *Kinpaku Aishi* (Gold foil interleaf paper) and has also recently started to produce processed papers.

Besides this, *Bitchu Washi* (*Kozo*, *Mitsumata* and *Gampi* paper) located in Kurashiki-shi, Okayama has a history of about 1000 years. Niimi-shi which produces *Takao Washi* (*Kozo* paper), *Ohtake Washi* (*Kozo* paper) produced in Ohtake, Hiroshima and *Tokuchi Washi* (*Kozo* paper) and Tokuchi-machi, Yamaguchi still remain in operation.

● *Tottori Prefecture*
Inshu Washi

This paper is made at Aoya-machi, Ketaka-gun and Saji-machi, Yasu-gun located in East Tottori and is the second largest producing center next to *Echizen* (Fukui) *Washi*.

It has a history over 1000 years and during the *Yedo* period (1603-1867) prospered as a supplier of paper officially designated by the clan. After the *Meiji* period (1867-1912) such daily use papers as *Shojigami*, copy base paper and office use papers were made in volume. After World War 2, papermakers switched to and developed and supplied calligraphy paper, *Chigiri-e yoshi* (paper for torn paper picture). The industry has always adapted to the changes in lifestyle of the general public. Therefore, products are diversified.

Gasenshi (calligraphy paper) and halt-size calligraphy paper are skillfully made by combining straw, miscanthus, bamboo and wood pulp with *Kozo* and *Mitsumata*. Therefore, it reproduces a sharp ink color and has a good reputation as a paper which has excellent expression of light and dark shades of ink. Also, art paper and processed *Kozo*, *Mitsumata* and *Gampi* papers are famous and appeal to the user because of their qualities of good design and color and dyeing technique.

● *Shimane Prefecture*
Izumo Washi

Izumo Washi is a general term for papers made in the Izumo area of Shimane. and at present, the following papers are made in the 3 areas of Izumo. Folkcraft paper (Yagumo-mura, Yatsuka-gun), *Hirose Washi* (Hirose-machi, Nogi-gun) and *Hiikawa Washi* (Mitoya-cho, Iishi-gun).

The origin of Izumo folkcraft paper is said to be from the *Heian* period (794-1192). The main materials are *Gampi*, *Kozo* and *Mitsumata* and among them, the unbleached *Gampi* paper made by Eishiro Abe (deceased) who was designated a Living National Treasure, was famous and even at present, his granchildren, the brothers Shinichiro and Norimasa are keeping up the tradition.

The characteristics of this paper is careful selection of raw material and with the aim of extracting only the pure paper fiber. By making most of its specific quality, they have succeeded in making an unrivalled beautiful *Washi*. There are also complete sets of many beautifully dyed papers.

Sekishu Washi, Sekishu Hanshi (cf. Glossary)

Sekishu Washi is made at the following 3 towns:at Misumi-cho, Naka-gun as the central producing area, Tsuwano-cho, Kanoashi-gun and Sakurae-cho, Ouchi-gun. *Sekishu Hanshi* is produced at Misumi-cho.

The origin dates back to the *Nara* Period (710-794) and in the *Yedo* Period (1603-1867), *Sekishu Hanshi* was the standard paper of the age with the Osaka market as the distribution center. *Kozo* is the raw material but it has a unique method of production. At the alkali boiling stage, the epidermis of the *Kozo* bark is not removed and great care is taken at the beating stage to separate the fibers uniformly, which aids in making a strong and beautiful paper.

The *Sekishu Hanshi* which is produced by the Sekishu Hanshi Technical Assembly, is designated as an Important National Intangible Asset and that technique has been carried on up to today. Recently, *Kozo* is the main raw material, but *Mitsumata* and *Gampi* papers and a wide variety of *Washi* processed goods are also produced.

Yasuro Hamatani

SHIKOKU AREA

Shikoku is an area which produces much paper. From the past, raw material has been cultivated and delivered to all parts of Japan. The volume of water in the rivers in Shikoku is abundant and it may be said that as a paper producing area, conditions of location are ideal.

For this reason, there are many handmade and machine-made paper mills located here. In Kawanoe-shi, Ehime, there are such large industries as Daio and Maruuzumi Paper Companies and at Ino-cho and Tosa-shi, Kochi, there are also many machine-made paper mills. There are no other areas in Japan where these mills in close proximity with handmade paper mills coexist and coprosper with each other.

93 *Washi* mills (no. of vats, 179) are located in the Shikoku area and in 1976, *Tosa* and *Awa Washi* and in 1977, *Oozu Washi* were designated National Traditional Industrial Art. While expressing their special qualities, these papers are preserving the traditional papermaking technique.

● *Ehime Prefecture*

In the Kawanoe area, there are 17 *Washi* makers mainly producing *Mozo Hanshi* and *Kairyo-shi* (cf. Glossary).

A large variety of raw materials are used and they are producing calligraphy papers, each of which have their special characteristic and it may be said that it is a production center where a mass production system is maintained. As mentioned before, there are many machine-made paper mills and next door to a large enterprise emitting smoke from a smoke-stack over 200 meters tall, *Washi* makers are making a living and this scene seems strange but at the same time, the difference between traditional industry and modern industry can be clearly understood.

In the Tooyo area, 17 paper mills produce *Hoshoshi* and *Danshi*. Crepeing of *Danshi* is a valuable technique born from tradition.

In the Ikazaki area (Kita-gun), there are 5 *Washi* mills which are making *Kozo* papers, Shojigami and calligraphy *Hanshi*. One mill has 15 vats lined up and is an imposing sight.

In Nomura-cho (Higashi Uwa-gun), a mill produces *Senka-shi* (cf. Glossary) which has been made from the past and even in Matsuyama-shi 1 mill remains which makes calligraphy paper.

● *Kochi Prefecture*

In the Takaoka area of Kochi-shi, there are 25 *Washi* mills which are producing *Shojigami*, calligraphy and art papers. In this area, compared to the past, the scale of *Washi* mills has become smaller but there are many younger generation papermakers who often play baseball together with the other young men of Ino-cho (Agawa-gun) and it may be said it is an area composed of three generations of papermakers.

In the Ino area, *Tengujo* (cf. Glossary), *Zubikishi* (tracing paper) and base paper for mimeograph use was produced in the past but due to the great change in office machinery, demand for these papers decreased sharply. However, recently, with "Tosa Washi Traditional Industry Hall as a center, the variety of *Washi* has increased and with traditional papermaking technique a fine texture *Washi* is being produced. At 12 *Washi* mills, mainly art paper and mounting paper are made and ultra thin papers which have been made from the past are also still produced.

Also, at Monobe-mura (Kami-gun) 3

Washi makers produce *Niraushi*, at Otoyo-machi (Nagaoka-gun) 1 mill makes *Iwahara-shi*, at Nangoku-shi, 1 mill makes *Gasenshi*, at Agawa-mura (Agawa-gun) 1 mill makes *Seichoshi* (cf. Glossary), at Hayama-mura (Takaoka-gun) 2 mills make *Suzaka Hanshi*, at Kubokawa-machi (Takaoka-gun) 1 mill makes *Shojigami* and at Hidaka-mura (Takaoka-gun) 1 mill makes *Kozo* papers adding up to a total of 10 mills. In these areas, cultivation of papermaking material is active, so the special traits of raw material is well known and a distinctive featured *Washi* is produced.

In this way, in Kochi, *Washi* mills are located throughout the whole area of the prefecture so the variety of *Washi* is great. But on top of that, it is a producing area where the 3 "makings" i.e. papermaking, raw material making (cultivation) and tool making are all assembled in one area.

● *Tokushima Prefecture*

In Tokushima there is 1 mill in Yamakawa-cho (Oe-gun), 3 mills in Kami Naka-cho (Naka-gun) and 1 mill in Ikeda-cho (Miyoshi-gun).

At the Yamakawa-cho mill, a great variety of dyed papers are made and has prospered together with the folkcraft paper boom. On the ceiling and walls of the International Scientific Exposition held in 1985, blue dyed paper and vegetable-dyed paper were used for decoration. In March, 1989, the Awa *Washi* Traditional Industry Hall was inagurated. It is an area where there are many subjects of interest regarding the *Washi* industry.

In this way, Shikoku is a paper producing area which has possibilities to grow larger in the future and further develop as a paper producing center.

Kenichi Miyazaki

KYUSHU AREA

It is said that *Washi* making spread to Kyushu during the *Bunroku* years (1592-1596) and was introduced by Saint Nichigen, a priest of the Nichiren Sect. At the Fukudai Temple in Chikugo-shi, Fukuoka (formerly Mizoguchi, Furukawa-mura, Yame-gun, Fukuoka) there is a monument inscribed with the words "The Birthplace of Kyushu Papermaking" written by Takeakira Enomoto (1836-1908, an important member of the *Meiji* government) and a statue of Saint Nichigen. Thereafter, it is said that the papermaking technique spread to the various areas in Kyushu.

The golden days of papermaking in the Kyushu area was 25 years from the end of the *Meiji* period to the beginning of the *Showa* period (1903-1928). The number of papermakers totaled 7000 and paper was exported to China and Korea. The highest peak of production was reached around the 2-3 year of *Showa* (1927-28) and after that, the number of papermakers and production decreased.

After World War 2, a temporary boom arose but due to the change in life-style of the general public, demand for *Washi* continuously decreased and at present, there are only 30 papermakers.

● *Fukuoka Prefecture*
Yame Washi (Chikugo Washi)

Yame Washi was originally called *Chikugo Washi* and its production was initiated by Saint Nichigen. This *Washi* has the oldest history and tradition in the Kyushu area. The characteristic is using as main raw material, the long-fibered *Kozo* indigenous to the Yame area and producing paper by skillful traditional methods. Therefore, the quality is elegant and strong and denies all attempts at imitation by other local papers.

This paper is favored widely in such uses as mounting paper, painting and writing paper, woodblock printing, folkcraft paper, industrial use, etc. and recently, a new demand area is being developed by production of processed items. In 1972, it was designated as Fukuoka Intangible Cultural Asset (industrial art technique) and in 1978, as Fukuoka Special Industrial Art.

● *Saga Prefecture*
Nao Washi

This paper developed as a side work of the farmers located in Nao, Yamato-cho Saga-gun who mainly produced lantern paper and at present, 3 papermakers are designated as Saga Cultural Assets.

Jubashi Washi

This paper also was a side work of the farmers located in Jubashi, Imari-shi and at present, there are 5 papermakers. They are designated as Imari-shi Intangible Cultural Assets.

This paper is used for lantern paper, mounting paper, calligraphy paper, etc. and cooperative work in the manufacturing process is being carried out.

● *Oita Prefecture*
Yayoe Washi

At Yayoe-cho, Minami Amabe-gun, *Shojigami*, umbrella paper and *Hoshoshi* are being produced and are designated as Yayoe-cho Intangible Cultural Assets. At present, development of products to meet consumer needs are carried out.

● *Miyazaki Prefecture*
Hokita Washi

At the Hokita area, north of Saito-shi, production of machine-made and handmade *Washi* is carried out on a small scale.

● *Kumamoto Prefecture*
Miyaji Washi

The tradition of *Miyaji Washi* produced at Miyaji, Yatsushiro-shi, is carried on by Hiroshi Miyata alone who is mainly making *Shojigami*. For that reason, the prefecture and Yatsushiro-shi are backing up the fostering of *Miyaji Washi*.

● *Kagoshima Prefecture*
Gamoo Washi

This paper is produced in Gamoo-cho, Aira-gun, and is used for *Shojigami* and mounting paper. They are also expanding production to include writing and painting paper.

● *Okinawa Prefecture*
Ryukyu Paper

At Takaraguchi Hikawa located in Gibo-cho, Shuri, Naha-shi, good quality water flowed forth and the Ryukyu royal government established a papermaking mill. Even after the royal government was annexed, Tosa paper artisans were invited and a modified paper mill was constructed but was destroyed by the disaster of World War 2 and ceased to exist. Eishiro Abe who participated in the Folkcraft Movement highly desired restoration of Ryukyu paper. His follower, Kimihiko Katsu, moved to Takaraguchi Hikawa in December, 1977, and attempted to restore Ryukyu paper production using the local *Plantain* (Musa Paradisiach) and green *Gampi* as raw material. He was successful and later increased the assortment of papers by utilizing local vegetation to make brilliant-colored dyed papers befitting to the tropical south island. These papers gathered much attention. However, in 1987, he passed away suddenly at the age of 40 and now, 2 of his apprentices (Meisei Ankei and Chosho Takayasu) are continuing his work.

Jitsumo Akiyama

GLOSSARY

Tesuki Washi	Handmade Japanese paper (*Washi*)
Kikaizuki Washi	Machine-made Japanese paper
Yoshi	Machine-made western-style papers

Main Raw Materials for Washi

Kozo	Broussonetia kazinoki Sieb., family Moraceae. General term for a variety of papermaking mulberries, characterized by strong, sinewy and long fibers.
Mitsumata	Edgeworthia papyrifera Sieb. et Zucc., family, Thymelaeaceae, genus Edgeworthia. Characterized by fine-grained, soft, pliant and lustrous fibers.
Gampi	Diplomorpha sikokiana Nakai, family, Thymelaeaceae, genus Diplomorpha. Harvested Feb. to May when water content is high. Characterized by fine and glossy fiber.
Kurara	Sophora angustifolia Sieb. et Zucc., perennial herbaceous plant of the lupinus family, fiber taken from bark of stems.
Asa	Cannabis sativa L.. Hemp

Mucilages

Neri	General term for the various kinds of vegetable mucilage used in *Washi*, such as that extracted from the *Tororo-aoi* root.
Tororo-aoi	Hibiscus manihot L. Medic. Annual herbaceous plant of the genus Abelmoschus of the Malvaceae family. Roots harvested between Nov. and early Dec. and crushed to make *Neri* mucilage. A relative of okra.
Nori-utsugi	Hydrangea paniculata, Sieb., grows to height of 6-10 ft, deciduous tree of the Saxifragaceae family. Inner bark used to make *Neri* mucilage.

Washi Producing Methods

Tamezuki (Accumulation papermaking)	"*Tame*" means to save, amass or accumulate, i.e. in that sense to settle. *Suki* or *Zuki* means the action to make paper so literally translated "fiber settling papermaking method". The ancient, original technique of scooping fibers, in which sheets are formed quickly and without use of mucilage by allowing the pulp stock to drain through the screen. In other words, *Tamezuki* is done by putting the right amount of material into the mold and allowing the solution to filter through while spreading it evenly.
Nagashizuki (Discharge papermaking)	"*Nagasu*" is the verb meaning to let flow or run. Literally translated "fiber flow papermaking method". This papermaking method peculiar to Japan, is characterized by ejecting excess pulp stock from the mold made possible by the use of *Neri*. In other words, *Nagashizuki* is done by repeatedly filling the mold and keeping the solution moving until one tosses out the final amount.

Tools used to make Washi

Keta	Wooden frame that holds the screen.
Su	Flexible screen, usually bamboo but sometimes miscanthus that acts as a sieve or strainer upon which the paper sheet is formed.
Sugeta	Papermaking mold; combination of *su* (screen) and *keta* (frame).
Sha	Fine screen, usually silk gauze; placed on top of a *su* to produce fine thin paper.
Suku	To make paper; as a prefix, the same character is read *suki* and as a suffix, -*zuki*.

Other special words

Dosa
Sizing solution made from animal glue and alum.

Shito
Literally "paper bed or floor". A stack of wet sheet *Washi*.

Sukashi
Watermark

Gofun
Chinese white or lime white, incinerated shell powder.

Kurokawa
"black bark" ; bark which has not been cleaned of its outer black layer.

Shirokawa
"white bark", inner bark cleaned of its outer black bark.

Washi products

Danshi
Literally "*Sandlewood* paper". Originated in the *Nara* period (710-794) and even currently used as high grade wrapping paper or for ceremonial rites. This is a *Kozo* paper, thick, elegant and white which ladies of the court preferred to write poems during the *Heian* period (794-1192). It was also called "*Michinoikugami*" which is synonymous with *Danshi*. The present *Danshi* is furrowed or creped but this is a comparatively new development. Used for ceremonial purposes today.

Fudagami
Literally "tag paper". Thick, water resistant tag paper used for labeling fabrics during dyeing. Coated with persimmon tannin to make it waterproof.

Fusumagami
Thick paper used for surface of *Fusuma* (sliding panel).

Gasenshi
Originally, a calligraphy writing and India ink drawing paper imported from China during the *Yedo* period (1603-1867). There were attempts to make Chinese-style *Gasenshi* which is characterized by subtle blurring of ink and a smooth brush touch. In *Mitsumata* paper producing areas, bamboo, straw and wood pulp were mixed and such paper as *Inshu* (Tottori) and *Koshu* (Yamanashi) *Gasenshi* were developed and are called *Wagasenshi* (domestic-made *Gasenshi*) in contrast to imported *Gasenshi*. Standard size 72.7 × 136.4 cm.

Hakuaishi
Literally, "interleaf paper for foil". 100% *Mitsumata* paper, used for packaging and preserving gold and silver foil.

Hakuuchishi
Literally. "foil beating paper". When beating out gold or silver foil, a small piece is placed between the sheet of paper and beaten. A special clay is used in this *Gampi* paper and Nashio (Hyogo) has been famous for its production from old times. Also made in Kanazawa (Ishikawa).

Hanshi
"Half-size sheet", originally half size of old *Sugiharashi* (25 × 35 cm). A paper of many uses, durable, thin, light and inexpensive. Used for calligraphy writing, account books, etc.. *Sekishu* (Shimane) and *Suruga* (Shizuoka) *Hanshi* have been famous from old times. Nowadays, such *Hanshi* as *Mozo* (imitation) and *Kairyo* (improved) *Hanshi* made from wood pulp and a mixture of other materials are produced. Standard size 24-26 × 32.5-35 cm.

Hodomurashi   The name is derived from the locality of production in Tochigi where papermakers still exist. The Karasuyama clan encouraged production of this *Kozo* paper and together with the *Nishinouchishi* produced in the neighboring Mito clan, it gained a high reputation. It is a little thicker than *Nishinouchishi* and is an old style *Tamezuki* paper but formed using *Neri*. Used for printing books.

Hoshoshi   A high grade *Kozo* paper. The original meaning of this paper is that oral orders or commands of the Shogun were written by secretaries or government authorities in his name on this paper and signed with official seal affixed. In the middle ages, this paper originated in Echizen (Fukui) and especially during the *Yedo* period (1603-1867) it was extensively used as official document paper. The reputation of *Echizen Hosho* is high and currently remains in use as woodblock print paper. Standard size 39.4 × 53 cm.

Hosokawashi   A catch-all name for *Kozo Washi* produced in Ogawa-cho, Saitama for permanent records, accounts, etc.. Originally a *Kozo* paper similar to *Sugiharashi* made in Hosokawa (Hyogo) was brought to *Yedo* and as the papermaking center of *Yedo* was Ogawa, the technique of the 2 papers were combined to make *Hosokawashi*.

Kaishi   Literally "pocket paper". A general term for paper used in the tea ceremony tucked in the front fold of the kimono. Used to clean the fingers after wiping the teabowl or as a plate for cakes or sweets served during the ceremony. Karasuyama *Kaishi* is famous and is used by the Imperial household.

Karakami   Literally, "Chinese paper". Patterned writing paper introduced from China.

Kamiko   Literally, "paper clothing". The *Kozo* paper is treated with persimmon tannin and after drying, it is crumpled thoroughly and then smoothed and tailored into a wearing apparel.

Katagami   Thick, durable paper cut into stencils. *Ise Katagami* is a stencil design cut in Ise. However, the base *Kozo* or *Mitsumata* paper is from Hiroshima or Gifu

Kinshi Ginshi Yoshi   100% *Mitsumata* paper, cut and twisted into yarn. The yarn is coated with gold or silver and used in Nishijin (Kyoto) brocade.

Komagami   Originally, a paper often used as a utility paper by women for wrapping or *Kaishi* and was decorated by a pretty design. The scope of application gradually developed from a small-size sheet to such large-size paper as panel paper with patterns designed in the wet sheet. Also called art paper.

Kyokushi Literally "bureau paper". In 1874, the Papermaking Dept., Printing Bureau, Ministry of Finance was established and efforts were made to make a unique Japanese-style paper. In 1878, this paper was exhibited at the Paris Exposition and widely acclaimed. A thick *Mitsumata* paper, smooth, strongly pliant with sharp reproduction printability.

Kumogami A paper with a cloud design. Used for long, narrow *tanzaku* and square *shikishi* poetry cards. A decorating technique of overlaying dyed fibers in a cloud design on the top and bottom part of the wet sheet. There are many variations of the technique.

Maniaishi A *Gampi* paper originating in the *Muromachi* period (1336-1573) and the name is derived due to the fact it can be pasted without any joint for half the width (90 cm) of a sliding panel Literally, it means "paper meeting requirements" or "paper serving the purpose". It is used for sliding panel paper, writing and drawing paper and backing paper for mounting. It is represented by *Echizen Torinoko* and Nashio paper using pulverized clay and is an example of development into a different grade of paper.

Michinoku-gami (cf. Danshi) Literally, means "paper from northern Japan" and the name appears often in books of lady authors during the *Heian* period (794-1192) together with paper made by *Shioku-In* (Kyoto government paper mill, established 806-810). It is a *Kozo* paper synonymous with *Danshi*. Used for ceremonial purposes such as writing, wrapping gifts, etc..

Minogami One of the oldest and most popular of a number of plain *Kozo* papers originally made in Mino, Gifu. *Minogami* family registers dated 702 still remain in *Shoso-In* which attests to its old history. The old *Minogami* standard size called *Minoban* was 33. × 24. 3 cm. Today, *Minogami* means a *Kozo* paper for stationary, books or *Shojigami* (sliding door paper).

Misugami History of the name is unknown. It is a thin *Kozo* paper used for mounting. At present made in Yoshino-cho, Nara. Pigment powder derived from incinerated clam shells is mixed with *Kozo* pulp and the paper is made in a small size papermaking mold. The characteristic of this paper is that it is immediately taken off the screen and dried on the drying board so it becomes a soft and mature paper.

Minatogami Wall paper pasted about a height of 60 cm from the floor on the lower part of the wall. Pasted on the wall to support it firmly. Exclusively used for tea ceremony houses.

Momigami Thick, high-quality *Kozo* paper often treated with the root of *Konnyaku* (devil's tongue) and crumpled, rubbed and stretched. Used for *Kamiko* (paper clothing).

Nishinouchi-shi A special *Kozo* paper encouraged by the Mito clan and the name is derived from the locale of production, Nishinouchi, Ibaragi. There are still papermakers here using the superior *Nasu Kozo* and the paper has a wide use and was famous as ballot paper during the *Meiji* period (1867-1912).

Ramonshi

"*Ramon*" originally means a thin silk textile. A decorated paper where the dyed fiber (*Gampi* etc.) is twilled and overlaid on the entire surface of the paper resembling the woven textile of "*Ramon*". This paper existed during the *Heian* period (710-794) but this gorgeous technique died out later and attempts to revive this paper continue.

Seichoshi

During the *Yedo* period (1603-1867), a ledger cleanly rewritten was called "*Sei-cho*". Therefore, a high grade *Kozo* paper for preserving such records came to be called *Seichoshi*. It was extensively made in Tosa (Kochi) and western Japan and at present, it is still produced in Agawa, Kochi.

Senkashi

During the *Tensho* years (1573-1592), the priest Senka devised this *Kozo* paper at the Anraku temple and the Uwajima clan encouraged production which flourished greatly. This strong and thick paper is made by scooping the stock onto a fine mesh and large mesh screen and doubled over joining 2 sheets into 1 thick one. Used for cover paper of books. Still made in Ehime and Kochi.

Senshi

A drawing paper praised by writers and artists from old times and the soft and gentle blurring effect has no comparison. Raw material is a mixture of fibers of Chinese *Spindletree* bark and rice straw.

Shifu

Literally, paper cloth. A 100% *Kozo* paper, soft and strong. The paper is cut and twisted into threads which are wove into paper cloth.

Shojigami

Traditional sliding door paper. *Shoji* is the latticed sliding door and the paper is pasted over the lattice work and used as panels. It permits light into the room while retaining the warmth. Standard size 63.6 × 93.9 cm.. This paper is a *Kozo* paper produced in various areas of Japan. The highest class of *Shojigami* is the *Shoingami*. With development of Japanese-style architechture for temples and samurai domiciles, the *Shoin* (study room) was established and the highest class paper for the sliding door was used for this room.

Sugiharashi

The name is derived from Sugihara-mura (Hyogo) at the end of the *Heian* period (794-1192). It is a *Kozo* paper representing the middle ages and samurai and priests often used this paper as gifts on formal occasions. This paper was not as thick as *Danshi* and it's simplicity was favored particularly by the samurai class. During the *Yedo* period (1603-1867) it also became popular among the common people.

Sukigata Moyooshi

Elegantly designed papers. Paper processed while still in a moist state to create a design or pattern. Originally, paper to write poetry or copy sutras. These ornate papers are still produced today with more new designs and patterns.

Sukushi

Recycled paper. Paper insufficiently deinked was called light inked paper or water clouded paper. Included in this category was *Kankonshi* (paper recalling the lost soul) which was paper recycled from letters of the deceased and recycled paper for daily use.

Tengujoshi In the middle ages, an extremely thin *Kozo* paper originating in Mino (Gifu). The origin of the name is unknown but uses the most sophisticated of papermaking techniques. Used for artist's tracing paper, block copy for wood-block prints, and backing paper but after the *Meiji* period (1867-1912), it was used for industrial papers such as typewriter paper, etc. and was made extensively in Mino (Gifu) and Tosa (Kochi). Still made in Kochi. Much is exported overseas where it is favored for wrapping material for precious stones, jewelry and pieces of fine art.

Torinoko A *Gampi* paper which appeared in the middle ages made primarily in Echizen (Fukui). *Torinoko* literally means "child of the bird or egg" but it must have been derived from the unbleached color of the paper resembling the color of the bird's egg of light yellow. Used for stationary and cards, art printing, sliding panel paper and semi-official documents.

Uchigumori A decorative technique of calligraphy paper with an overlay of dyed fibers lying like a stretch of clouds on the upper and lower edge of the paper. There are such varieties as blue clouds, purple clouds and blue and purple clouds. The overlay fiber is now *Gampi* but in the past *Kozo* fibers were used. There is also a technique which is used to express stormy water movement.

Udagami The name is derived from Uda-gun, Nara. Used for mounting. A rather thick *Kozo* paper containing local clay which gives softness to the paper and prevents stretching or shrinking.

Yoshinogami A thin *Kozo* paper made in Nara which is most suitable for lacquer filtration.

Prefecture	Organization	Representative	Secretary	Area Code	Address	Tel.
Iwate	Higashiyama Washi Trade & Industry Cooperative A'ssn	T.Suzuki		029-03	Nagasaka,Higashiyama-cho,Higashi Iwai-gun, Iwate Pref.	0191-47-2424
Niigata	Echigo Washi Promotion A'ssn	K.Ito	K.Kobayashi	959-44	Koide,Kamikawa-mura, Higashi Kambara-gun, Niigata Pref.	025495-2920
Tochigi	Karasuyama Washi Promotion Society	K.Fukuda		322-06	Chuo-2chome, Karasuyama-cho, Nasu-gun,Tochigi Pref.	02878-2-2028
Ibaragi	Ibaragi Washi Agricultural Cooperative A'ssn	G.Kikuchi		319-31	Aza Morozawa, Yamagata-cho,Naka-gun, Ibaragi Pref.	02955-7-2061
Saitama	Saitama Ogawa Washi Industry A'ssn	A.Tanaka		355-03	1-230 Oaza Ogawa, Ogawa-cho,Hiki-gun, Saitama Pref.	0493-72-0079
Yamanashi	Nishijima Handmade Paper Industrial Cooperative A'ssn	T.Kasai	C.Kasai	409-33	1-391 Nishijima, Nakatomi-cho,Minami Koma-gun,Yamanashi Pref.	055642-2519
Nagano	Nagano Handmade Washi Promotion Society	T.Abe		380-00	c/o Industrial Laboratory, 188-Wakasato,Nagano, Nagano Pref.	0262-26-2812
Shizuoka	Ishikawa Paper Co.	F.Ishikawa		421-33	3-1325 Kita Hamano, Fujikawa-cho,Ihara-gun Shizuoka Pref.	0545-85-2226
Shizuoka	Yuno Handmade Washi Studio	T.Naito		418-04	Kamijo, Kami Yuno, Shiba kawa-cho, Fuji-gun, Shizuoka Pref.	05446-6-0733
Toyama	Toyama Washi Cooperative A'ssn	K.Yoshida		939-23	1-691 Kagami-cho, Yatsuo Machi, Nei-gun, Toyama Pref.	0764-55-1818
Ishikawa	Ishikawa Washi Promotion Society	S.Sakamoto		920-11	Futamata-cho, Kanazawa, Ishikawa Pref.	0762-4-3024
Gifu	Mino Handmade Washi Cooperative A'ssn	S.Goto	T.Mame	501-37	777 Maeno,Mino,Gifu Pref.	0575-33-1241
Fukui	Fukui Washi Industrial Cooperative A'ssn	M.Ishikawa	M.Takeyasu	915-02	11-11 Ohtaki, Imadate-cho, Imadate-gun,Fukui Pref.	0778-43-0875
Fukui	Wakasa Washi Production Cooperative A'ssn	S.Shiba		917-03	6-1 Watada, Obama, Fukui Pref.	0770-59-0131
Shiga	Naruko Paper Studio	T.Naruko		520-21	930 Kiryu-cho, Kamitagami, Ohtsu, Shiga Pref.	0775-49-0323
Kyoto	Kurodani Washi Promotion Society	K.Fukuda	T.Fukuda	623-01	Kurodani-cho,Ayabe, Kyoto	0773-44-0213
Kyoto	Tanaka Paper Industry Co.	M.Tanaka		620-03	Aza Futamata, Oe-cho, Kasa-gun, Kyoto	0773-56-0743
Nara	Hiroyuki Fukunishi			639-34	Kubokakiuchi,Yoshino-cho, Yoshino-gun, Nara Pref.	07463-6-6513
Hyogo	Tanitoku Paper Co.	T.Tanino		669-11	1492 Nashio,Shiose-cho, Nishinomiya,Hyogo	0797-61-0224
Hyogo	Kami-cho Sugiharashi Research Institute	M.Inoue		679-12	733 Toba Kami-cho, Taka-gun, Hyogo Pref.	07953-6-0080
Tottori	Tottori Handmade Washi Trade A'ssn	H.Shio	Z.Kadowaki	680	c/o Industial Laboratory, 390 Akisato,Tottori, Tottori Pref	0857-22-8322
Shimane	Izumo Folkcraft Paper Cooperative A'ssn	S.Abe		690-21	1727 Higashi Iwasaka, Yagumo-mura, Yatsuka-gun, Shimane Pref.	0852-54-0303
Shimane	Sekishu Washi Cooperative A'ssn	Y.Nishida		699-32	1548 Furuichiba, Misumi-cho, Naka-gun, Shimane Pref.	08553-2-1141
Yamaguchi	Yamaguchi Washi A'ssn	K.Yamauchi		747-05	826 Shimachi, Tokuchi-cho, Saba-gun, Yamaguchi Pref.	08355-4-0106
Tokushima	Awa Handmade Washi Trade & Industry A'ssn	M.Fujimori		779-34	136 Aza Kawahigashi, Yamakawa-cho, Oe-gun, Tokushima Pref.	0883-42-2035
Ehime	Iyo Handmade Washi Promotion Society	H.Ishikawa		779-01	Kamibun-cho,Kawanoe, Ehime Pref.	0896-56-3232
Ehime	Tooyo Handmade Washi Promotion Society	S.Sugino		799-13	941 Kuniyasu, Tooyo, Ehime Pref.	0898-66-1122
Ehime	Ohzu Handmade Washi Cooperative A'ssn	A.Numai		795-03	928 Hiraoka Ko, Ikazaki-cho, Kita-gun, Ehime Pref.	0893-44-2002
Kochi	Kochi Handmade Washi A'ssn	Y.Morita	T.Ueda	780	110 Asahi-cho 3-chome Kochi, Kochi Pref.	0888-73-5898
Fukuoka	Yame Handmade Washi Union	E.Takayama		834	2-123 Oaza Honcho 2 Banchi, Yame, Fukuoka Pref.	09432-4-3941

Impressions of the Translator/K. Fukushima

In the preface by Chairman Taki, it mentions that this "Handbook on the Art of *Washi*" is written in plain and simple language easily understood by the layman. Trusting these words, I undertook the request for translation from Mr. Shohei Asano in May, 1990. Little did I know then what I was in for.

Working for a paper company for some years and frequently visiting the "Paper Museum" located in Oji, Tokyo in my spare time, I was interested in and had some knowledge of *Washi* acquired from the exhibits displayed there. However, due to the long historical background of *Washi*, many unforeseen translation difficulties cropped up, necessitating more deeper and broader study on the various aspects of this traditional art. It was only with the warm encouragement and assistance of friends and colleagues that this translation was able to see light.

As the original articles are a condensed form of replies to basic questions put to experts in this field, I am not quite sure whether this immature translation is able to convey the quintessence of this cultural treasure which the experts so desired to express in between the lines of their short replies. However, it would be my greatest pleasure if this translation is able to trigger an increase of foreign *Washi* enthusiasts and stimulate a desire for further research in this matter.

In ending, I would like to express my deepest apprecation for the kind cooperation and timely advice given me by Mr. Asano, personnel of the Paper Museum and especially Mr. Richard Flavin (*Washi* papermaker, residing in the paper center of *Washi*, Ogawa, Saitama) for his helpful and pertinent suggestions.

February, 1991.

Translator, Kurio Fukushima

Born 1919 in Oakland, California, U.S.A., residing there until the age of 14. 1943, graduated English Literature Department, Tohoku University, Naval Reserve Student. At end of war, Foreign Language Instructor, Naval Academy. 1948, employed by Oji Paper Co.Ltd. and worked in Liaison Dept., Construction Office, Research Laboratory, Export Sales and Senior Staff member prior to retirement in 1989. Participated in various international conferences.

For any enquires on this book or *Washi*, please contact Mr. Shohei Asano, Wagami-do, 6-33-4 Hakusan Bunkyo-ku, Tokyo. 〒112 Tel. 03-3813-7117 Fax. 03-3813-8299

ALL KINDS OF JAPANESE PAPER

- All Printing Use
- Etching
- Greeting Cards & Envelopes
- Conservation
- Paper Serviettes
- Fancy Wrapping Paper
- Fancy Paper Products

MORIKI PAPER COMPANY, LTD.

4-24 HIGASHI-TERAO, TSURUMI-KU, YOKOHAMA, 230 JAPAN
Telephone:(045)583-2321
Telex No. : 3822595 PAPEX J
Cable Address: "PAPER YOKOHAMA"
Telefax : (045)583-1045
Representing(Sales in Europe) : Japanpaper Import Ges. Drissler & Co.,
                              Frankfurt/Main, West Germany
Representing(Sales in USA and Canada) : A/N/W-Crestwood
                              New York, U. S. A.

Japanese Hand Made Paper Shop

Come and see us about Japanese paper.
For prints, paintings, calligraphy
and other art projects

〒104 2-6-10, YAESU, CHUO-KU, TOKYO, JAPAN
Tel. 03 (3281) 1667/8537

YAMADA SHOKAI

Genuine Handmade
Japanese Paper Specialist

- *We have been in business for 330 years!*
- *Our showroom is huge, covering 360m²*
- *Visit our gallery of antique papers.*
- *You will be amazed at our selection*

小津和紙博物舗
OZU WASHI HAKUBUTSUHO
(OZU GALLERY)

2-6-3 Nihonbashi-Honcho Chuo-ku, 103

TOKYO 03- **3663-8788**

FAX: TOKYO (03) 3663-9460

Japanese handmade paper preserves nature

KOCHI PREF. HANDMADE PAPER COOP UNION

3-110, ASAHI-MACHI, KOCHI-SHI, 780, JAPAN

TEL   0888-73-5898   FAX   0888-72-5218

TOSA-WASHI

INO—CHO PAPER MUSEUM

110-1, SAIWAI-CHO, INO-CHO, AGAWA-GUN, KOCHI-PREF., 781-21, JAPAN

TEL   0888-93-0886

An Abridged Chronological Table of Washi

Period	Year	Main Historical Events
	China, Former Han Period (202 BC-14 AD)	From the ruins of Sian, Central Asia and surrounding areas, pieces of hemp paper were recovered.
	China, Latter Han Period (105)	T'sai Lun made paper from tree bark, hemp, old rags and macerated fish nets and became famous. His paper was called T'sai Ko-shi. (Distinguished T'sai's paper)
	China, Three Kingdoms (3rd to 4th Century)	From the ruins of Roran in Central Asia, words written on Hemp papers were recovered by Hedin and Stein and the condition of paper a 100 years after T'sai Lun can be confirmed. At that time, it was estimated that papermaking technique spread to such neighboring countries as Korea and Viet Nam.
	(548)	The King of Pekche (Korea) sent Buddhist statues and sutras written on paper to Japan. (official introduction of Buddhism to Japan)
	18th year of Suiko (610)	Doncho, a priest of Kokuryo (Korea) introduced painting material, paper-making, India ink manufacture and a water-powered mill to Japan and since then, was considered the forefather of Washi. At present, it is estimated that artisans from Korea started papermaking during the time not earlier than the reign of Empress Suiko. (592-628)
	1st year of Temmu (673)	At the temple of Kawahara in Asuka (Nara), young monks were summoned to copy the Issai-Kyo (complete collection of Buddhist Scriptures). This is the beginning of copying of sutras which later became a flourishing activity.
	1st year of Taiho (701)	The Taiho Ritsuryo (laws and regulations) was established and it stipulated that the Bureau of Scriptorial Matters should carry out papermaking and that the populance should deliver paper as a tax obligation.
	2nd year of Taiho (702)	The age of the oldest paper in Japan which could be ascertained i.e. family registers of paper made in Mino (Gifu), Chikuzen (Fukuoka) and Buzen (between Fukuoka and Oita) remain in Shoso-In. These papers for government use produced in each locality, left their individual characteristics.
Nara Period (710-794)	3rd year of Wado (710)	The seat of government was moved to Heijokyo (Nara). During the Nara period,

	1st year of Hoki (770)	Washi ... government ... copying ... made fr... processe... dyes an... using g... produce... A milli... and the... The Mi... Buddhis... inside o... matter ... (The gr... scriptur...
Heian Period (794-1192)	During the years of Daido (806-810)	In Kyot... mill) wa... the wor... period, ... paper.
	2nd year of Konin (811)	The wr... clearly ... Nagash... This in... time fro... (around... Nagash...
	7th year of Engi (907)	The En... was sti... should ... local an...
	3rd year of Ten-ei (1112)	Around ... Poems" ... complet... paperm... Glossar... decorat... highest ... was col...
Kamakura Period (1192-1333)	3rd year of Kenkyu (1192)	Yorito... Kamak... Deman... the mid... made pa... the capi... and cha...
	1st year of Shokyu (1219)	Among ... tradition... favored ... Glossar... samurai...
Muromachi, Azuchi and Momoyama Period (1336-1603)	During the years of Eisei (1504-1511)	The for... convert... 1396 bu... there w... paper).
Yedo Period (1603-1867)	8th year of Keicho (1603)	Ieyasu ... Tokuga... the Yed... became ... supplied... paperma... industry... correspo... bounds a... masses.
	Kan-ei Period (1624-1644)	Echizen ... designate... paper an... named G... designate... had their ... house.

veloped, centered upon
nt use paper and paper for
utras and beside white papers
m hemp, Kozo and Gampi, paper
for dyed paper using vegetable
pigments for decoration use
d and silver leaf were also

miniture pagodas were made
ldest printed matter in Japan i.e.
on Pagoda Dharani (a mystic
incantation) were contained
these pagodas. The oldest printed
the Muku Joko Dai Dharani
t innocent, pure-light Dharani
) printed in Silla (Korea).

Kamiya-In (government paper
established which succeeded to
started in Nara. During this
ere were 25 local areas making

en papers remaining in Shoso-In
ow the characteristics of the
ki method (curling of edges).
ates that during the passage of
the Nara to the Heian period
0) the technique of the
ki method developed.
hiki began to be compiled. It
ated in detail that Kamiya-In
ke 20,000 sheets per year and 42
s paid crop taxes with paper.
is time, "The 36 Selected
ishi Honganji manuscript) was
The Sukimoyoo (artistic
ing) such as Uchigumori (cf.
and technical methods of
as Suminagashi (marbling), the
ade of papermaking technique
ted and completed for this book.

Minamoto establishes the
Shogunate government.
r Washi increased greatly in
-age feudal society and locally
r was transported in volume to
An assortment of highly practical
cteristic papers were marketed.
e old aristocratic class,
Danshi (cf. Glossary) was
t the use of Sugiharashi (cf.
spread widely throughout the
ass.

r site of Kamiya-In was
to rice paddies and fields in
e paper artisans who worked
making Sukushi (recycled

kugawa establishes the
Shogunate government. During
Period, the general public also
nsumers and Washi was
volume at low cost. Therefore
ng became an important
Also, the amount of
ence increased by leaps and
d literacy grew among the

oshoshi (cf. Glossary) was
Shogunate government use
the papermaker was officially
yoshi Sukiya (government
papermaking house). Each clan
own designated papermaking

Period	Year	Event
	7th year of Kanbun (1667)	Suho clan (Yamaguchi Pref.) established a paper warehouse in Osaka. After that, influential clans each built their own paper warehouses.
	6th year of An-ei (1777)	Seichiku Kimura published a book titled "Shifu" (Paper notes). The domestic warehoused paper was assembled in the Osaka market and this book indicates that papermaking developed throughout Japan and formed an important industrial sector.
	10th year of Kansei (1798)	Chihei Kunisaki published the "Kamisuki Chohoki" (A handy book on papermaking). This is a practical manual on papermaking.
	1st year of Man-en (1860)	Genta Yoshii of Kochi Pref. invents the large-size paper mold. Later, many modifications of tools and papermaking methods were carried out and sized papers and copy papers which met the demand of the new age were made.
Meiji, Taisho and Showa Period (1868-1989)	1st year of Meiji (1868)	Meiji Restoration Coping with the new society, initially Washi competed with western-style papers and met the demand and also pioneered such papers as those for industrial use but this decreased gradually and a review of the real value of Washi was undertaken.
	7th year of Meiji (1874)	Yukosha, a western-style paper company started operation in Tokyo and 6 other companies followed suit in Osaka, Kyoto and Kobe.
	8th year of Meiji (1875)	A papermaking department was established within the Paper-Note Bureau, Ministry of Finance and papermakers of Echizen (Fukui) paper were invited to their Oji Mill in Tokyo.
	11th year of Meiji (1878)	At the World Exposition held in France, the Government Printing Bureau exhibited pure Mitsumata Torinoko (cf. Glossary) paper which earned a high reputation.
	30th year of Meiji (1897)	Genta Yoshii published "Nippon Seishi Ron" (A Treatise on Papermaking in Japan". A complete collection of various improvements.
	36th year of Meiji (1903)	According to government statistics, the number of papermaking house-holds reached an apex of 68,562 which gradually decreased later. Since 1872, when the education system was promulgated, state textbooks for primary grade schools used Washi but changed to western-style machine- made paper and school children became accustomed to this paper. Around this time, the Government Printing Bureau switched over to machine production of paper leaving currency paper only to be produced by hand.
	35th year of Showa (1960)	Bunsho Jugaku and Eishiro Abe start a 3 year investigation of paper among the National Treasures stored at Shoso-In. In 1970, a report on findings, "Papers of Shoso-In" was published.
	43rd year of Showa (1968)	Echizen Hosho (cf. Glossary) made by Ichibei Iwano and Gampi paper made by Eishiro Abe qualify for the designation of Important Intangible Cultural Assets and hereafter, conservation of traditional technique in papermaking as a cultural asset was recognized.
	50th year of Showa (1975)	Inshu (Tottori Pref.) Washi designated as Traditional Industrial Art. Promotion of papermaking as a Traditional Industrial Art was recognized.
	58th year of Showa (1983)	International Paper Convention held in Kyoto.